The Open University

T357
Structural integrity:
designing against failure

BLOCK 2
FRACTURE MECHANICS

PARTS 3 AND 4

This publication forms part of an Open University course T357 *Structural integrity: designing against failure*. Details of this and other Open University courses can be obtained from the Student Registration and Enquiry Service, The Open University, PO Box 197, Milton Keynes MK7 6BJ, United Kingdom: tel. +44 (0)845 300 60 90, email general-enquiries@open.ac.uk

Alternatively, you may visit the Open University website at http://www.open.ac.uk where you can learn more about the wide range of courses and packs offered at all levels by The Open University.

To purchase a selection of Open University course materials visit http://www.ouw.co.uk, or contact Open University Worldwide, Michael Young Building, Walton Hall, Milton Keynes MK7 6AA, United Kingdom for a brochure. tel. +44 (0)1908 858793; fax +44 (0)1908 858787; email ouw-customer-services@open.ac.uk

The Open University
Walton Hall, Milton Keynes
MK7 6AA

First published 2007.

Edited and designed by The Open University.

Typeset by SR Nova Pvt. Ltd, Bangalore, India.

Printed in the United Kingdom by The University Press, Cambridge.

ISBN 978 0 7492 1854 6

1.1

PART 3
DEFORMATION AND
FAILURE OF MATERIALS

CONTENTS

1 INTRODUCTION

The way that the stress state within a component influences how it fails was illustrated in Block 1 Part 3; in this part, we will delve a little deeper, initially at a microscopic level, into the mechanistic processes that drive these failures.

I will concentrate mainly on fracture, because this is often the defining characteristic of a 'failure'. I have already mentioned plastic collapse as a failure mechanism, where a material's yield stress is exceeded and deformation ensues; we will return to plastic collapse in Part 5. The mechanisms that lead to plastic collapse are the precursors to ductile fracture.

The mechanisms that give a material strength and toughness have their origins on the microscopic scale; these mechanisms interact with the applied stresses, and large-scale defects such as cracks, to produce the final property profile for a material. Processes such as fatigue, which often manifest themselves as apparently brittle crack growth, actually have their origins in small-scale plasticity.

Much of the behaviour and properties of materials is dependent on the defects that they contain. Glass is an extremely strong material, but in everyday use that strength is compromised by fine scratches on its surface. The strong, hard particles that strengthen aluminium alloys on a sub-micrometre scale are also the initiation points that lead to their failure when they are heavily deformed.

Although for most design purposes a knowledge of the mechanisms that underpin materials failure is not necessary (after all, the point is really to design a component not to fail), it is valuable to know something about the inner workings of the materials we use every day, and why they have the properties that they do.

Before we move on to look at these mechanisms, it is worthwhile reflecting on how plasticity arises in metals: see ☑ **Dislocations and plasticity** ☑.

☑ Dislocations and plasticity

The origins of plasticity lie at the atomic level in metals. Metals have a regular crystal structure, with the atoms packed closely in a repeating array. Figure 3.1 shows an example.

One of the defining properties of metals is that they exhibit plasticity when they are deformed, i.e. a stress greater than their yield stress will cause a permanent deformation. This does not happen with ceramic materials, for example, which tend to fail by a brittle fracture once their strength is exceeded.

In order for a metal to deform plastically, material (i.e. atoms) has to be moved around. The easier it is for atoms to move, the more ductile a metal will be. The real secret of the high ductility of metals lies in the presence of imperfections in the structure, which are known as *dislocations*.

Dislocations are found in practically all crystalline materials, but where metals differ from, say, ceramics is that the dislocations in metals can move when subjected to a force. When a metal is strained beyond its yield point, into the plastic regime, the dislocations move in response to the shear stress resulting from the applied load. The aggregate of this atomic-scale movement of very large numbers of dislocations is what we recognize as macroscopic plastic flow of the metal. Thus, two things are needed for plasticity in crystalline materials: the presence of dislocations and the ability for them to move through the crystal lattice. ▷

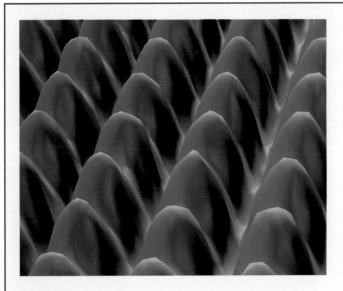

Figure 3.1   Atoms on the surface of nickel, imaged using a scanning tunnelling microscope. The image shows the regular positioning of the atoms; the 'shape' of the atoms is not real, but is an artefact of the method used to produce the image

Pure metals can be deformed to very large strains indeed: up to several hundred per cent. Alloying of metals is done partly to restrict the movement of dislocations, thus increasing the strength and reducing the ductility.

During plastic deformation, the shear forces in the material become high enough to 'move' dislocations. Dislocations are really just 'gaps' in the lattice; so, what actually happens is that atoms sequentially jump into the gap, as shown in Figure 3.2. In metals, there can be a staggeringly high number of dislocations, so that when many of them move in response to an applied stress, whole planes of atoms can be displaced relative to each other. This process is known as *slip*.

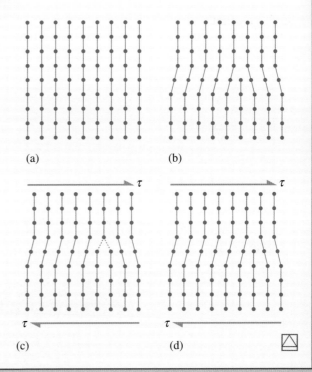

Figure 3.2   (a) A perfect crystal with no defects; (b) a crystal with a dislocation; (c) and (d) as the crystal experiences a shear stress, the bonding between atoms can be broken locally, so allowing the dislocation to 'move' through the crystal

Hopefully this should be revision for you from previous study. If not, what you need to take away from this is that plasticity occurs in metals by slip of the atomic planes, and the dislocations are what allow this to take place.

2 FRACTURE MECHANISMS IN METALS

Simple fracture, i.e. the separation of a piece into two parts, occurs in response to an applied load exceeding the material strength, generally at temperatures that are low relative to the melting point of the material. Two fracture modes are prevalent in simple fracture, i.e. ductile and brittle, and these are identified by the presence (or absence) of plastic deformation during fracture. Of the two, ductile fracture is generally better for the structural integrity of a component for a number of reasons:

- Brittle fracture (also known as cleavage) can occur very suddenly and without warning, because the final failure is rapid; during ductile fracture, however, plastic deformation indicates that fracture will shortly ensue.

- More energy is required to generate ductile failure, i.e. there is considerable plastic deformation of the material before final failure; as a consequence, materials that exhibit ductility are generally tougher.

Figure 3.3 illustrates three types of tensile fracture.

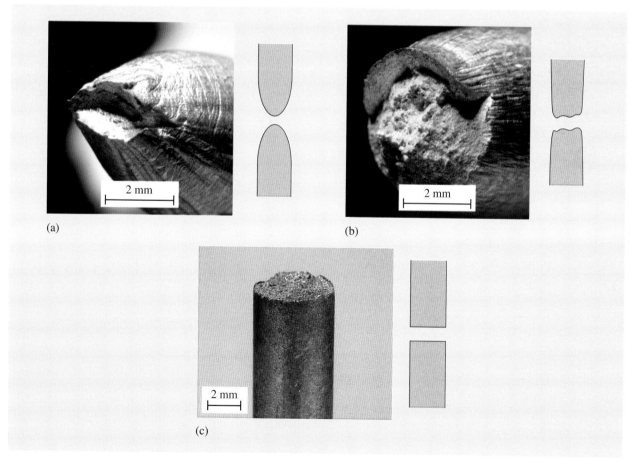

Figure 3.3   (a) Highly ductile fracture typical of a pure metal and (b) ductile fracture typical of an engineering alloy, both of which show necking; (c) brittle fracture showing no evidence of necking

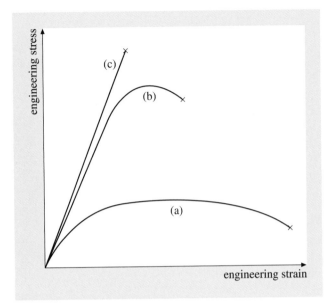

Figure 3.4   Uniaxial stress–strain curves for (a) a pure or very soft material; (b) an engineering metal; (c) a material with no ductility

The generation of a stress–strain curve from a material is covered in the 'Testing of materials and structures' programme on the course DVD.

Figure 3.4 shows the corresponding stress–strain graph for each of these types of failure. During ductile failure, plastic deformation leads to the formation of a neck shortly before failure. Figure 3.4(a) shows extreme ductility and is typical of pure or very soft metals only. Figure 3.4(b) is typical of most engineering materials, where work hardening has taken place prior to final fracture. Figure 3.4(c) shows brittle failure with the absence of any plasticity.

2.1 Ductile fracture

Ductile fracture during tensile loading proceeds in a number of stages:

- Stage I – isolated small cavities or microvoids form within the material.

- Stage II – the microvoids increase in size during the continued straining of the material.

- Stage III – the microvoids continue to grow during deformation and eventually coalesce to form a crack, which then propagates to cause failure.

A dislocation tangle occurs when the stress fields of dislocations moving on different planes within the material interact so as to stop the dislocations from moving. If the deformation energy can't be dissipated by dislocation motion a microvoid may form.

Figure 3.5(a) shows particles and grain boundaries in a metal before straining. During Stage I of ductile failure, the formation of microvoids occurs as a result of plastic flow during the onset of necking. These microvoids form at discontinuities in the metal, such as at inclusions or precipitates, as illustrated in Figure 3.5(b). Such particles are too hard to deform along with the metal and act as stress concentration sites where microvoids can form at the particle–metal interface. Also, dislocation tangles can generate sufficiently high stresses to initiate a microvoid, and stress concentrations at grain boundaries can cause isolated microvoids to form at boundaries.

In Stage II, as the straining of the metal continues, the microvoids increase in size, and further plastic deformation occurs as the material between the voids is strained, as illustrated in Figure 3.5(c).

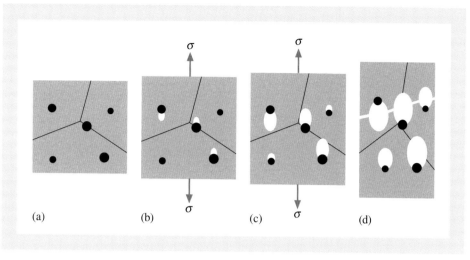

Figure 3.5   The process of microvoid coalescence to form a crack: (a) particles and grain boundaries in material before straining; (b) microvoids are formed at features during straining; (c) microvoid growth by further straining of material between microvoids; (d) coalescence of microvoids to form a crack

In Stage III, the microvoids continue to grow during deformation and eventually join together in a process known as microvoid coalescence to form a crack, as illustrated in Figure 3.5(d); this leads to final failure as the metal finally fractures into two separate parts.

The overall process from necking to final fracture during a tensile test is illustrated schematically in Figure 3.6.

Plastic deformation is driven by shear stresses in the material. We have seen with the aid of Mohr's circle that the maximum shear stress acts on a plane inclined at 45° to the directions of the largest and the smallest principal stresses (which in a uniaxial tensile test are the applied stress σ_1 and zero respectively). So we would

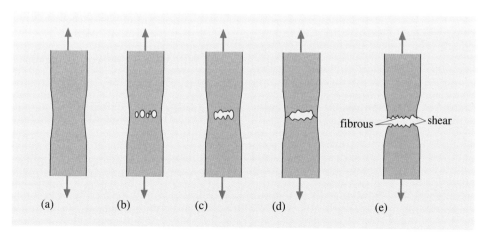

Figure 3.6   Stages in fracture due to microvoid coalescence: (a) initial necking; (b) formation of microvoids; (c) coalescence of voids to form a crack; (d) crack propagates through the specimen; (e) final failure: shear lips at 45° to the tensile stress are developed at the surface

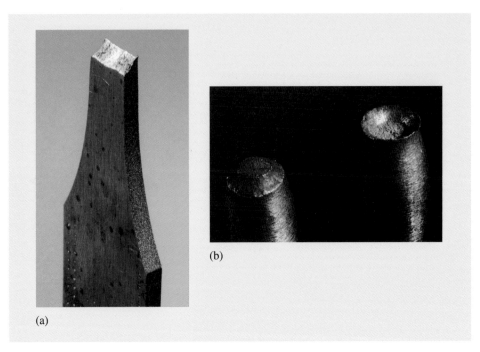

(b)

(a)

Figure 3.7   (a) A ductile fracture on a plane of maximum shear stress in aluminium loaded in tension; (b) cup-and-cone fracture in mild steel loaded in tension

expect ductile shear fractures to occur on a plane carrying the largest shear stress. For example, Figure 3.7(a) shows a fracture surface that is inclined at 45° to the direction of applied load. You may recall that the region of 45° fracture is aptly called a 'shear lip', and it can occupy any proportion of the fracture surface, depending on the material, the dimensions of the component and the conditions (e.g. temperature) prevailing during fracture. In Figure 3.7(a), the entire fracture surface consists of a 45° shear lip, but this occurs only in components with narrow cross sections. When the cross section is thick and circular, a shear lip forms around the circumference. This gives rise to a 'cup-and-cone' fracture (Figure 3.7b), in which one half consists of a flat-topped cone and the other half is a cup of complementary shape.

Microscopically, a ductile fracture surface has a dimpled appearance, where each dimple forms as a consequence of the development of a microvoid (Figure 3.8a); often, the defect that caused the void to form can be observed at the root of the dimple, as shown in Figure 3.8(b). The sharp ridges that surround the dimple are formed by metal that has necked to a point locally, in the same way as shown in the tensile test specimen in Figure 3.3(a).

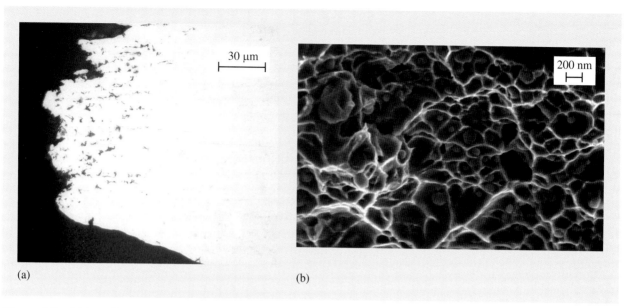

Figure 3.8   (a) Ductile voids near a fracture surface; (b) high-magnification micrograph of a stainless steel composite that has failed by microvoid coalescence: notice the particles at the base of the microvoids, which have nucleated the microvoids

2.2 Brittle fracture

Brittle fracture occurs by rapid crack propagation and without any appreciable plastic deformation prior to fracturing. It is found that most brittle fractures are of an 'opening' kind, where the two fracture surfaces simply separate as a result of an applied stress that exceeds the tensile strength of the material. As you might expect, in isotropic materials such fractures are controlled by the magnitude of the maximum tensile stress and the direction of crack growth is perpendicular to the direction of the applied stress.

The measured fracture strength to cause brittle failure is less than that predicted using theoretical calculations based on the strength of the atomic bonds holding the material together. This is because the tensile strength of a brittle material is controlled largely by the presence of scratches or microscopic crack-like defects that always exist within or on the surface of the material. These crack-like defects act as stress concentrators and magnify the effect of the applied stress.

A brittle fracture surface is distinguished by the absence of virtually all plastic deformation. If the two broken pieces are brought back together they should fit together quite well and the sample would appear to be practically undeformed. Similarly, on a microscopic scale, there should be no signs of the craters and ridges that are a feature of ductile fractures.

Brittle fracture in crystalline materials occurs by the breaking of interatomic bonds along particular atomic planes within the material; this process is referred to as *cleavage*. The fracture surface will depend upon the microstructure of the particular material. In polycrystalline materials, such as metals and ceramics, the fracture path will be either *between* the grains (*intergranular*; Figure 3.9a) or *across* the grains (*transgranular*; Figure 3.9b), and in either case the fracture surface will tend to be quite faceted (Figure 3.9c). In glassy or amorphous materials the cleavage fracture

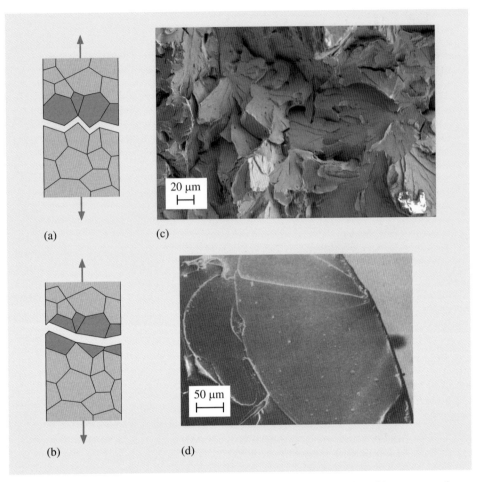

Figure 3.9   (a) Intergranular failure, which follows grain boundaries; (b) transgranular failure, which cuts across grains; (c) scanning electron microscope (SEM) micrograph of low-carbon ferritic steel, failed through cleavage; (d) a brittle failure in glass

surface does not have multiple facets; rather, it is generally smooth (Figure 3.9d) with long, curved markings that indicate the absence of a granular structure.

On both transgranular and glassy fractures there are often features called *river lines*, which resemble a river and its tributaries. These features are simply steps between smaller cleavage or crack-growth planes and can be very useful because they allow the direction of crack growth to be found; the crack grows in a 'downstream' direction (Figure 3.10).

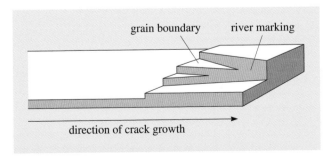

Figure 3.10   The formation of river markings

3 FATIGUE FAILURE

We have covered the fatigue process extensively in Part 2: a crack is initiated, usually at some point of stress concentration, and then propagates through the material. Although there is localized plastic flow around the fatigue crack, a fatigue-fracture surface is characterized by a lack of gross surface deformation, and there is no change of shape of the component from bulk plasticity.

3.1 Fatigue-fracture surfaces

In Block 1 Part 3 you saw that the appearance and orientation of a fracture surface may suggest the state of stress that caused fracture, and whether the fracture was ductile or brittle. Fatigue-fracture surfaces can be equally revealing: although they are macroscopically flat and smooth, the fracture surfaces resulting from fatigue frequently contain telltale markings. Figure 3.11 shows a typical example; it is a photograph of the fracture surface of a bend specimen (such as you saw in Part 1) that has eventually failed during cyclic tensile loading.

You can see that the surface consists of two distinct zones separated by the line labelled AB, which indicates the line of the crack front prior to final fracture.

The zone below AB is relatively dull and corresponds to the area over which the crack has grown under cyclic loading. The faint lines that are parallel to the notch front are called 'beach markings', so called because they resemble the patterns left on a beach by the retreating tide. Beach markings are generated by changes in loading conditions, e.g. the magnitude or frequency of the loading, and are normally visible to the naked eye. They are very useful in tracing back the origin of crack initiation; in this case the specimen had a sharp starter notch. In some cases the beach marks are made visible by corrosion of the material (successive marks being corroded by different amounts). The brighter zone above AB is the surface of the final overload fracture.

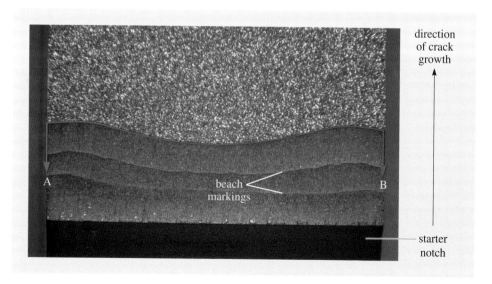

Figure 3.11   The markings on a fatigue-fracture surface (the width of the specimen is 25 mm)

An important principle worth noting at this point is that the *presence* of beach markings is an unambiguous symptom of fatigue, but the *absence* of such markings does not *necessarily* mean that fatigue did not occur. In practice, fatigue surfaces can become worn or corroded long before the final failure event.

3.2 Micromechanisms of fatigue

The process of fatigue can be divided into two distinct stages:

1   crack initiation

2   crack propagation.

3.2.1 Crack initiation

In some cases crack initiation may be a fait accompli, even before cyclic loading begins. Opportunities abound for introducing crack-like features into a component during manufacture, e.g. during welding and machining (Figure 3.12). We saw in Part 2 how the surface condition of a component can influence its fatigue life: Figure 3.13 shows the *S–N* curves for specimens that are identical except for the preparation of their surfaces.

In material that was originally free of cracks or defects, initiation may occur at grain boundaries and second-phase particles.

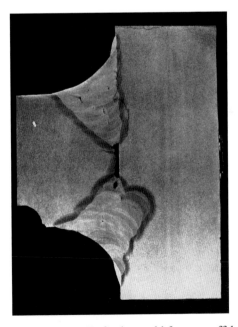

Figure 3.12   Defective weld from an offshore platform

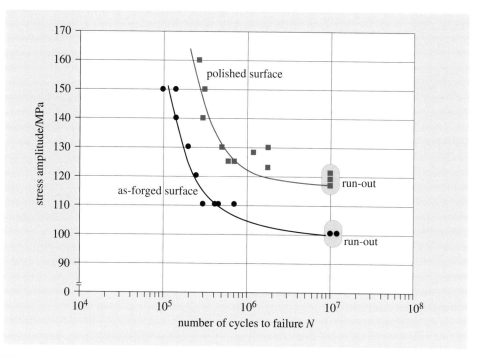

Figure 3.13 An illustration of the effect of surface condition on the number of cycles to cause failure of specimens of a low-alloy steel. The as-forged surface offers more sites for the initiation of a fatigue crack

But we also know that fatigue cracks can be initiated on smooth, polished surfaces; this occurs by the formation of ▽ **slip bands** ▽, which eventually turn into cracks. Initiation occurs primarily at the surface because the material is not as constrained as it is within its bulk, and dislocations in the atomic structure that are mobile can move through to the surface, creating the microscopic steps that eventually become slip bands.

▽ Slip bands

The atomic structure of crystalline materials (e.g. metals and their alloys) is highly ordered, with planes of atoms stacked in regular, repeating sequences. The bonding that holds the atoms together, and their crystal structure, has a strong influence on a material's properties.

The yield stress of the material is essentially determined by the force required to begin plastically deforming the crystals. The plastic deformation of crystalline materials occurs when one part of the crystal is displaced with respect to another part along a particular atomic plane. This process of movement is called slip, which is the most common mechanism for plastic deformation in crystalline materials. Slip generally occurs in directions in which the atoms are most closely packed, since this requires the least amount of energy, and it occurs as a result of shear stresses.

The slip mechanism in a *perfect* crystal is illustrated in Figure 3.14. A block of the crystal is subjected to a shear force (Figure 3.14a). The atomic lattice at first strains elastically; this is equivalent to the linear portion of the stress–strain curve. On removing the applied stress the lattice will recover to its original position. When the shear stress reaches a critical level, the elastically stretched bonds between atoms break, allowing atoms to move within the crystal ▷

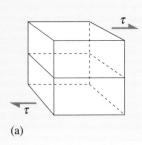
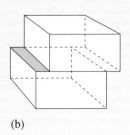
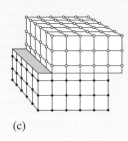

(a)   (b)   (c)

Figure 3.14 Progressive discrete 'slip' of planes of atoms past each other within an atomic lattice

(Figure 3.14b) and form new bonds to adjacent atoms (Figure 3.14c).

The shear force necessary to produce permanent deformation by the mechanism described above is much greater than that required for the permanent deformation of most real materials. This is because in real materials the slip process is aided by the movement of *defects* (which are often just vacancies, 'gaps' where there are missing atoms) through the crystal structure. This allows the slip to occur in an incremental manner; a few neighbouring atoms in a plane at a time suddenly undergo slip by jumping into their next site. This has the overall effect of displacing a plane of atoms relative to an adjacent plane. The crystal defects that make it possible for crystals to slip (or 'glide') are called *dislocations*. Dislocations are in fact 'line defects' – a series of vacancies along a line, rather than a single defect.

The slip process in a real crystal can be described by the movement of dislocations as shown in Figure 3.15(a)–(c). Provided that the loading is maintained, the process is repeated and the dislocation moves progressively through the structure. There is no simultaneous, large-scale breaking of bonds within the structure, or a coordinated movement of atoms, just local shifting of the bonds between atoms. And, although the passage of a single dislocation might well be considered to have a negligible effect in a crystal during plastic deformation of a metal, there are great numbers of dislocations on the move, all contributing, a few atoms at a time, to the overall plastic change of shape.

It is this large-scale movement of dislocations that leads to the formation of slip bands. Figure 3.16(a) shows a compressed crystal of niobium, where the dislocation movement associated with plastic compression has caused large macroscopic steps on the sample surface. Slip does not occur on every atomic plane within a crystal, but rather is confined to localized slip planes, generally where the atoms are closely packed. In Figure 3.16(b) you can see that slip has occurred on a number of adjacent slip planes; this is also illustrated schematically in Figure 3.16(c). Each concentrated 'packet' of slip is called a slip band. This tendency for slip to be localized into bands occurs under both unidirectional and cyclic loading. The formation of these 'slip steps' on a surface can lead to the initiation of fatigue cracking.

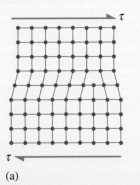
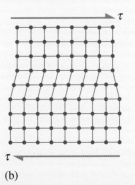
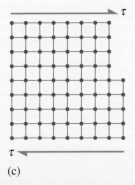

(a)   (b)   (c)

Figure 3.15 The series of steps as a dislocation moves through a crystal lattice

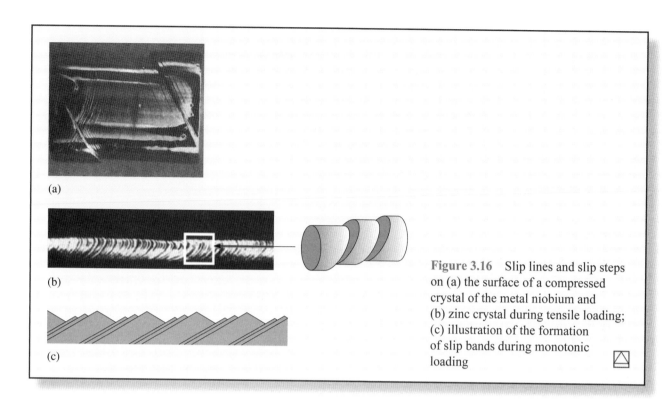

(a)

(b)

(c)

Figure 3.16   Slip lines and slip steps on (a) the surface of a compressed crystal of the metal niobium and (b) zinc crystal during tensile loading; (c) illustration of the formation of slip bands during monotonic loading

The fact that dislocation motion, i.e. the source of plastic deformation, occurs in a metal at stresses far below its yield stress, as measured during a standard tensile test, may be confusing. However, this is because the measurements in a tensile test are relatively coarse and are unable to detect the highly localized movement of dislocations within near-surface grains that happen to be suitably oriented to experience the maximum shear stress.

Under cyclic loading, so-called 'persistent slip bands' form. These promote increased dislocation activity in the region and can lead to the formation of microscopic slip steps on the surface of the material. Continued cyclic loading eventually results in the formation of *extrusions* and *intrusions* (Figure 3.17a). Figure 3.17(b) illustrates how the extrusions and intrusions are formed: slip operates on different planes in different directions, depending on the applied stress, but it is not reversible. So there is a 'ratchet' mechanism that allows intrusions and extrusions to develop. The stress concentration effect of these extrusions and intrusions (particularly the intrusions) can cause fatigue cracks to initiate from them.

Figure 3.18 shows the initiation of a fatigue crack from a slip band on the smooth, electrochemically polished surface of an aluminium alloy specimen. Although the slip band developed very early in the fatigue loading of the specimen (Figure 3.18a), the formation of a fatigue crack at the slip band took a considerable number of cycles. After 300 000 cycles the fatigue crack is just visible using a scanning electron microscope (SEM) (Figure 3.18b). It had grown to a surface length of about 30 μm after 750 000 cycles (Figure 3.18c). Once a fatigue crack forms, though, it speeds up; ΔK at the crack tip increases as the crack becomes longer, unless the loading is changed.

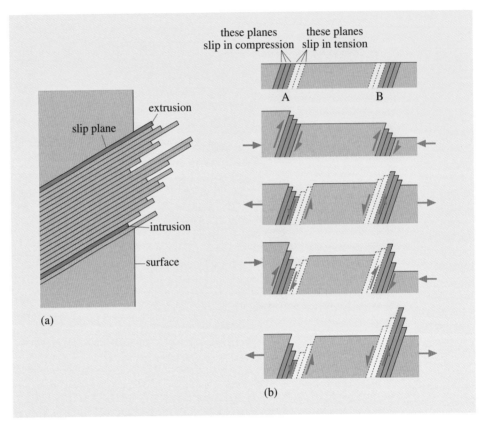

Figure 3.17 (a) Extrusions and intrusions developed during cyclic loading; (b) initiation of a fatigue crack on a smooth specimen surface by the generation of slip steps

This mechanism for crack initiation on external surfaces (including at the root of notches) has also been proven by experiments, where the complete removal of persistent slip bands by deep electropolishing from time to time during the cycling of the specimen leads to an infinite fatigue life.

So this is the explanation of how fatigue cracks can form where no crack previously existed: the movement of dislocations akin to what happens in bulk plastic deformation, but on a much smaller and more localized scale. And, if the surface is rough, then the chances are that it will contain stress concentrations at which slip bands will form preferentially.

However, it would be wrong to imply that all fatigue cracks are nucleated in this way. In many materials, cracks may be nucleated at inclusions, as illustrated in Figure 3.19, or at porosity within the material.

I think I have now gone far enough with a rationalization of slip bands and crack initiation. My aim has been to give you a qualitative picture of how fatigue cracks nucleate. A vast amount of dislocation theory exists that is concerned with models of fatigue initiation processes. But for the purposes of this course it is not necessary for you to study these models; and, anyway, it would require a much more detailed knowledge and understanding of dislocations and their behaviour. So now we will investigate how a crack, having initiated, propagates and grows to a critical length that can eventually cause failure.

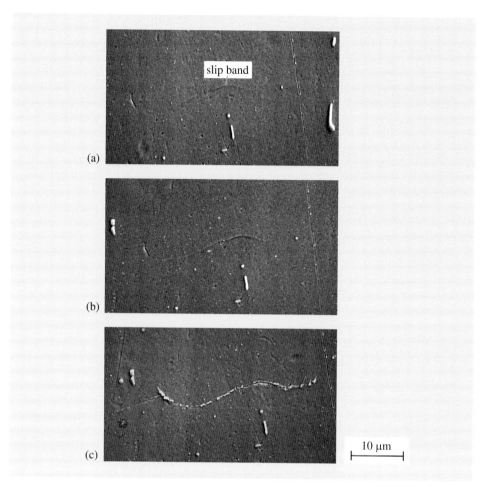

Figure 3.18   Fatigue-crack initiation along a slip band on the polished surface of aluminium after (a) 10 000 cycles; (b) 300 000 cycles; (c) 750 000 cycles

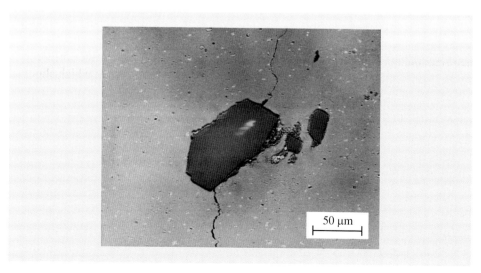

Figure 3.19   Crack initiating from an inclusion in an aluminium alloy

3.2.2 Crack propagation

In general, we can identify two stages in the overall process of crack propagation. In *Stage I growth* the crack continues to advance along the slip band in which it started, i.e. along a plane of maximum shear stress, usually at 45° to the applied stress. When a typical crack has crossed a few grains in this manner, which may take thousands or even millions of load cycles to achieve, depending on the stress amplitude, it changes direction and tends to move on a plane perpendicular to the direction of the largest principal stress. Crack propagation in this new direction is called *Stage II growth*. The two stages of crack growth are illustrated schematically in Figure 3.20(a). Figure 3.20(b) shows an example of the two stages of crack growth in an Al–Zn–Mg alloy.

Stage I can be regarded essentially as an extension of the initiation process, in which the crack advances by linking up the fatigue damage present in the slip band.

If the tensile stress is high, Stage I growth may not be observed at all. This is often the case in engineering components that contain stress concentrations, such as machined surfaces at screw threads or defects due to welding; in such components, Stage II crack propagation is the dominant factor in failure by fatigue. A further general observation is that Stage II growth dominates in polycrystalline materials because Stage I cracks usually terminate when the crack running along a slip band encounters a grain boundary, as grain boundaries act as obstacles to slip.

So Stage II crack growth is the controlling factor in the fatigue failure of most engineering components. Stage II crack growth itself is controlled primarily by the stress intensity at the tip of the advancing crack: recall from Part 2 how the growth rate of a long crack can be related to the stress intensity range by the Paris equation.

Propagating cracks produce *striations* (or ripples) on Stage II fracture surfaces, i.e. small ridges that run perpendicular to the direction of crack growth (Figure 3.21).

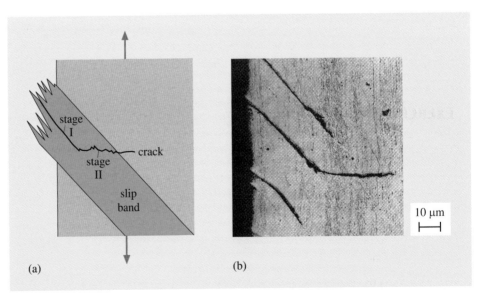

(a)   (b)

Figure 3.20   (a) Stage I and Stage II fatigue-crack growth, where the crack has nucleated at an intrusion in a slip band; (b) optical micrograph of an electropolished section of an aluminium alloy, showing the transition from Stage I to Stage II crack growth

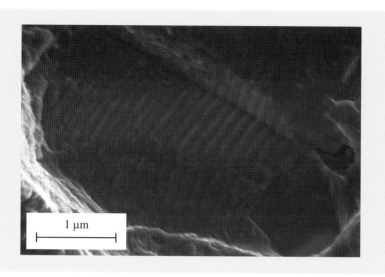

Figure 3.21   Fatigue striations on the Stage II fracture surface of a steel-based composite

These could be considered to be microscopic versions of the macroscopic beach markings described earlier, although the mechanisms that produce them are entirely different. Ductility appears to be the key to well-defined striations; the lower the ductility of a material, the less obvious are the striations.

It has been found experimentally that each striation on the fatigue surface is produced by a single stress cycle, for fatigue cracks that are growing in the Paris regime, i.e. with the stress intensity range not too close to the fatigue threshold and the peak stress intensity not too close to the fracture toughness. The presence of striations is an exclusive characteristic of fatigue: they define unambiguously that failure has occurred by fatigue. However, just as for beach markings, although the presence of striations means fatigue, the absence of striations does not necessarily mean no fatigue – for example, if the ductility of the material is too low for a ripple of plastic deformation to be produced at a crack tip, or if striations are obliterated by the fracture surfaces rubbing together during compression parts of the load cycle.

EXERCISE 3.1

If the striations in Figure 3.21 were produced by successive load cycles, what is the approximate growth rate of the crack (in units of metres per cycle)?

The actual mechanism of striation formation is again related to plasticity, i.e. the local movement of dislocations around the crack tip. Figure 3.22 illustrates the generally accepted mechanism for crack growth, involving the formation of striations as the crack advances.

In Figure 3.22(a) there is no load on the specimen; the ridges correspond to striations that have already formed. In Figure 3.22(b) a small tensile load is applied, causing the crack to open and shear stresses to develop at the tip. When the tensile load is

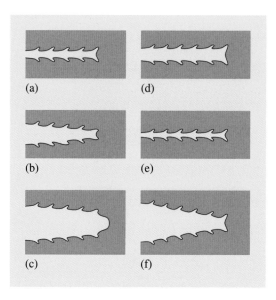

Figure 3.22   Striation formation by a process of plastic blunting

(a) (d)

(b) (e)

(c) (f)

increased (Figure 3.22c), plastic flow occurs at the crack tip, with the result that the crack is both extended and blunted. Localized slip occurs at an angle of ±45° to the crack plane. When the specimen is unloaded (Figure 3.22d), the crack begins to close, and the material that was plastically deformed in tension experiences a compressive force as the crack closes; the shear stresses (and hence the direction of slip) are reversed. At the lowest load the crack is nearly closed (and therefore 'sharper') and the material at the crack tip flows inwards to produce the 'ears' shown in Figure 3.22(e). These ears correspond to new striations on the fracture surface. From Figure 3.22(a)–(e) you can see that the fatigue crack grows by one striation during one cycle of loading. Figure 3.22(f) is the beginning of the next cycle (like Figure 3.22b). This process is repeated during subsequent loading cycles, with each cycle producing a striation on both the lower and the upper crack surfaces. This gives a striation spacing that is equal to the crack growth per cycle, da/dN.

In general, the crack continues to grow until either it becomes unstable and rapid fracture ensues, or the remaining cross section of the material cannot sustain the applied load and failure occurs by plastic collapse. The value of K_{IC} will determine the conditions and mode of the final failure, which brings us back to the role of fracture mechanics in fatigue-crack propagation that we considered in Part 1.

SAQ 3.2 (Learning outcome 3.3 and revision)

(a) Summarize the part played by plastic deformation in (i) fatigue-crack initiation and (ii) fatigue-crack propagation.

(b) Suggest what would be the consequences for fatigue if plastic flow in a material could be inhibited (i.e. if the yield strength could be increased).

SAQ 3.3 (Learning outcomes 3.1, 3.2 and revision)

Figure 3.23 shows a fatigue failure of an aluminium wheel hub from a racing car.

(a) Identify the point(s) where the fracture started, any features that reveal the failure was driven by fatigue and the region that was last to break.

(b) Suggest the type of loading that led to this failure.

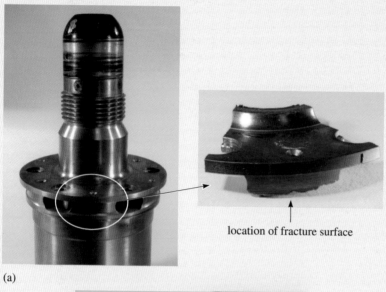

location of fracture surface

(a)

(b)

Figure 3.23   (a) Aluminium wheel hub showing location of fracture; (b) close-up of fracture surface

4 FAILURE MECHANISMS IN NON-METALS

Metals are ubiquitous in structural applications, as they offer the best combination of strength and toughness for carrying high loads. But polymers and ceramics have equally important roles to play, although polymers cannot match the strength and high-temperature capability of metals, and ceramics fall far short of them in toughness. This section outlines the structure of these non-metallic materials and the general mechanisms that are responsible for their failure.

4.1 Polymers under stress

The structure of polymers differs from those of metals and ceramics. Polymers are made up of long 'chains' of atoms, with other atoms and groups of atoms attached. The individual chains are held together by very strong atomic bonds; whereas bonding between the chains tends to be much weaker, so the chains can move relative to each other fairly easily. Hence, polymers have lower strength and stiffness than metals and ceramics.

Generally, the structure of most polymers is a combination of regions where the chains are randomly disordered (i.e. amorphous regions) and areas where they are aligned and packed closely (i.e. crystalline regions). Although these regions are called 'crystalline', there are only weak bonds between the chains, so such regions are not 'true' crystals, as are found in metals for instance. A typical structure is shown in Figure 3.24. Such a structure is called 'partially crystalline'. The degree of crystallinity depends on the precise type of polymer and its processing history.

When a partially crystalline polymer is loaded in tension, a point is reached beyond which plastic strain commences and permanent deformation occurs. As with metals, increasing plastic strain eventually leads to necking in the specimen. However, unlike in metals, the necked region does not keep shrinking up to the point of failure. Instead, once the neck has formed, the section of the neck remains constant and the neck simply grows longitudinally along the specimen. You can demonstrate this to

Figure 3.24   A typical structure of a polymer, showing crystalline regions surrounded by amorphous regions

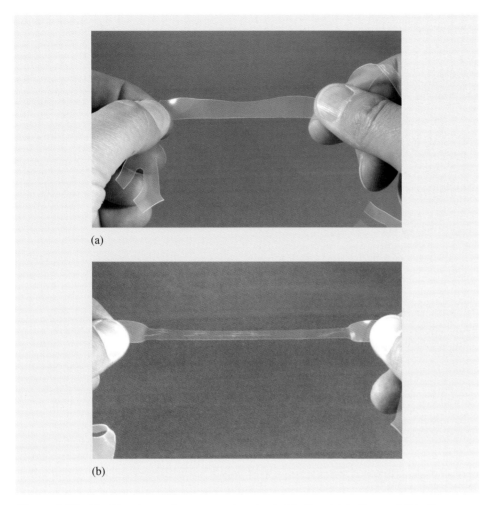

(a)

(b)

Figure 3.25   Necking in a polymer sample: plastic binding (a) before and (b) after necking

yourself by pulling the plastic binding typically found around cans of beer or fizzy drinks. A very long neck can be obtained (Figure 3.25).

Why can such a long neck be sustained? It is all to do with the structure of the polymer. Under small stresses, the amorphous regions deform by the molecules sliding over one another. This has the effect of partially aligning the crystalline regions and crystallizing the amorphous regions.

At higher stresses, the crystalline regions also start to become unravelled and become aligned along the loading axis; because all of the polymer molecules are lining up with the applied stress, the degree of crystallinity in this fibrillar structure is now greater than in the original lamellar configuration. The stages in this process are shown in Figure 3.26.

Eventually, at even higher stresses, the polymer chains are unfolded and extended to form a highly crystallized form of the polymer, as illustrated in Figure 3.27.

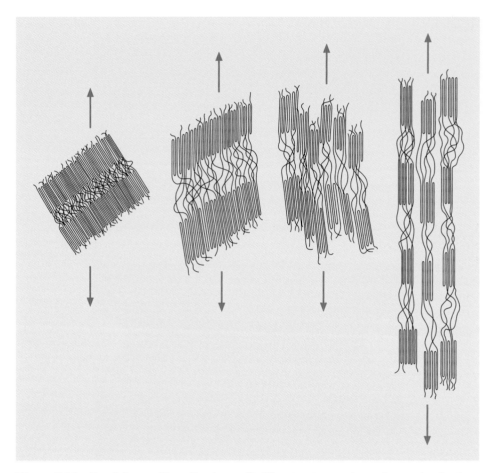

Figure 3.26   Breakdown of lamellae into a fibrillar structure under an increasing load

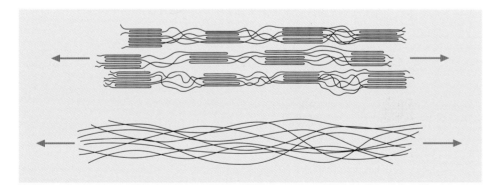

Figure 3.27   Final stage in the breakdown of fibrils, as they are unfolded and extend to form long chains in the fully cold-drawn condition

The polymer is now in a condition where all the chains (with their strong bonding) are aligned with the applied stress. In this condition the polymer has a much higher strength and stiffness than in its initial, partly amorphous state.

How do these mechanisms influence yielding, fracture and fatigue?

4.2 Fracture of polymers

The process just described, where the polymer molecules slide relative to one another under an applied stress, is known as shear yielding. As the stress increases further, failure eventually occurs when the load exceeds the strength of the crystallized structure.

Polymers can also yield by a process called 'crazing', where yielding occurs in very localized regions that lead to cavitation (similar in nature to microvoid formation in metals). Crazing occurs when voids form between the aligned molecular chains. Voids form at any structural discontinuities, such as impurities and porosity. Craze formation is illustrated schematically in Figure 3.28.

Crazes are not cracks in the true sense, because the aligned molecules can continue to sustain loads after they are formed, as shown in the SEM micrograph in Figure 3.29. Fracture finally occurs when the fibrils are unable to support the applied stress and they rupture. Crazing is often observed in highly strained regions during bending, which you may have noticed in the transparent polymers that are used to make rulers and bodies of ballpoint pens; shiny, crack-like defects can be seen if they are observed in a bright light.

Both of these mechanisms can occur in a polymer, and the one that dominates is dictated by a number of factors such as:

- the molecular structure
- the stress state
- the temperature.

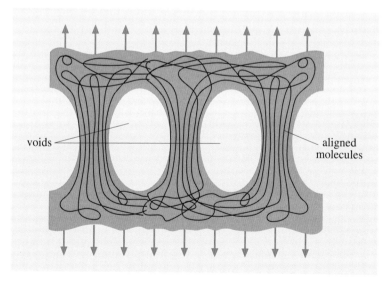

Figure 3.28 Craze formation in a polymer. As the fibrils are formed, voids nucleate at discontinuities; as the stress is increased, more material is drawn into the fibrils and the craze width increases

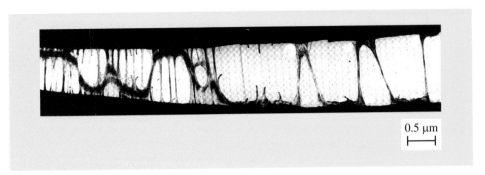

0.5 µm

Figure 3.29   SEM micrograph of a thin section through a craze in polystyrene showing bridging fibres

4.3 Fatigue of polymers

As with metallic materials, crack growth by cyclic fatigue is problematic in polymers; but fatigue in polymers can be further complicated because of ☑ **viscoelasticity** ☑. This can lead to heating at the crack tip, which changes the local properties of the polymer.

☑ Viscoelasticity

Some materials – such as many polymers – show 'time-dependent' elastic behaviour, where their response to an applied load is not instantaneous (as it tends to be with metals at room temperature) but evolves over a measurable time. And, although in the elastic regime the strain is recoverable, the stress–strain curve is not the same for loading and unloading (Figure 3.30).

Such materials are said to exhibit *viscoelasticity*, as their response to an applied load involves both elastic and viscous components, which at normal loading and unloading rates leads to the hysteresis shown in Figure 3.30. The energy absorbed during one loading–unloading cycle is given by the area within the loop, and it is the dissipation of this energy that can lead to a rise in temperature when

viscoelastic materials are subjected to cyclic loading. The shape of the loop depends on the rates of loading and unloading (unlike normal time-independent elasticity).

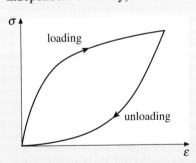

Figure 3.30   A typical hysteresis curve of a viscoelastic material

Depending on the nature of the polymer, there are two possible mechanisms that can allow fatigue cracks to develop.

If the polymer is relatively brittle (perhaps because extensive ☑ **cross-linking** ☑ inhibits crack-tip plasticity), then bonds within the molecular chains can be broken during cyclic loading, leading to progressive crack growth. Figure 3.31 shows a typical fatigue failure from the plastic handle of a pair of scissors. Here the crack, which probably initiated as a result of a stress concentration due to rusting of the

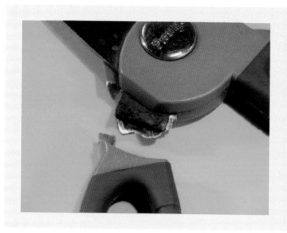

steel tang

fatigue surface

fast-fracture surface

Figure 3.31   (a) Fracture of a scissor handle; (b) a closer view of the fracture surface: the fatigue surface is highlighted by the darker area and the fast-fracture region is white

'stainless' steel blade, has grown until the remaining material is insufficient to maintain the applied load and rapid fracture has occurred.

The other main mechanism is by viscoelasticity at the crack tip. The strain energy dissipated in the material as it cycles round the hysteresis loop creates heat. Because of the relatively low thermal conductivity of polymers, this heat is not readily dissipated. If the rate of heat production becomes higher than the rate of heat dissipation, then the temperature of the material at the crack tip will rise. If the temperature rise is sufficiently high, then the material at the crack tip may exceed the melting point, which can result in local melting and viscous flow. As a consequence, some material is removed from the crack-tip region, thereby allowing the crack to advance.

▽ Cross-linking

Polymer materials are made up of many individual 'chains' of atoms, usually having a 'backbone' of carbon atoms with other atoms or groups of atoms stuck on to the sides of the chains. In addition to the bonds that hold the atoms in the chains together, many polymers form bonds *between* neighbouring chains, creating a three-dimensional network (Figure 3.32). The cross-linked bonds are just as strong as the bonds between atoms in the chain. The effect on properties is that heavily cross-linked polymers are hard and brittle because the cross-linking prevents movement between the molecular chains.

Polymers can become brittle over time, as the effects of UV radiation lead to the formation of cross-links that were not present when the material was manufactured.

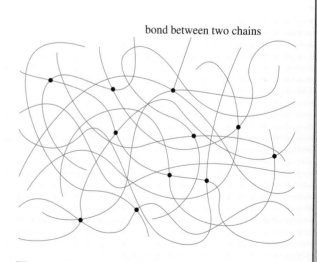

bond between two chains

Figure 3.32   Cross-linked polymer chains

4.4 Ceramics

4.4.1 Fracture of ceramics

Ceramics, like metals, also form crystalline structures at the atomic scale. However, in ceramics, the nature of the bonding between the atoms means that they like to stay where they are relative to their neighbours. Dislocations cannot pass through the crystal structure as they can in a metal and, hence, there is little or no slip possible, with the result that ceramics are extremely brittle compared with metals.

A typical, simple overload fracture surface of a ceramic material (alumina) is shown in Figure 3.33: there is a combination of both transgranular fracture, where individual grains fracture, and intergranular fracture, where the fracture path is along grain boundaries. This is similar to cleavage fracture in brittle metallic materials; because of the inability of ceramics to deform plastically (dislocation movement cannot occur), there is no evidence of any plastic deformation.

Figure 3.34 shows the difference between an indent in a metal and one in a ceramic. In the metal, the indent is accommodated by plastic deformation (Figure 3.34a); in the ceramic, the stresses induced by the indent are not relieved by plastic deformation and the elastic stress field is high enough to cause cracks to propagate (Figure 3.34b): so-called Hertzian cracking (after the scientist Heinrich Rudolf Hertz, 1857–1894, who provided solutions for contact stresses).

4.4.2 Fatigue of ceramics

In ductile materials that satisfy ☑ the von Mises criterion for slip ☑, crack growth takes place in two stages: Stage I growth, where initial crack growth is initiated by slip bands, and subsequent Stage II growth, where cracking is due to irreversible plastic deformation causing progressive sharpening and blunting of the crack tip, thereby advancing the crack.

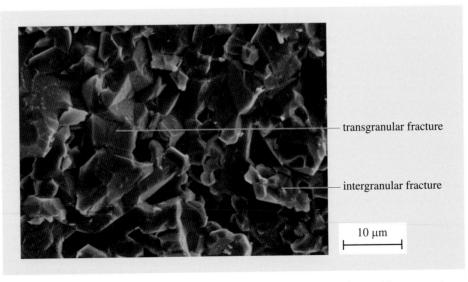

Figure 3.33   Fracture surface of alumina showing both transgranular and intergranular fracture

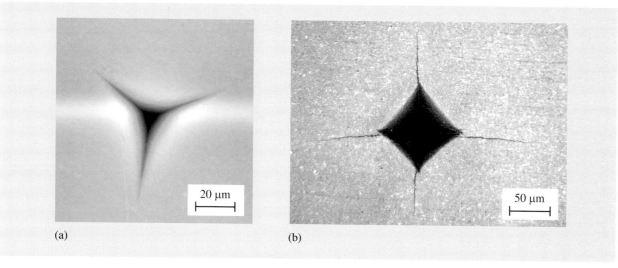

Figure 3.34 (a) Indentation in a metal is by plastic deformation; (b) in ceramics, the indentation leads to cracking of the material; note that the indenter used on the metal was triangular, while that used on the ceramic was diamond-shaped

☑ The von Mises criterion for slip

When slip occurs on a large scale within a crystal, there are local changes of shape of the grains within the material because of the large-scale generation and movement of dislocations. If the crystalline grains are to accommodate this slip without cracking, each grain must deform such that it remains in contact with its neighbours. What this effectively means is that slip must be able to take place in more than one direction. Von Mises (remember him from Block 1?) showed that the minimum number of independent slip systems (i.e. directions within a crystal grain where dislocations can move freely) is five if the material is to be able to deform plastically; any fewer than this means that the material will be brittle.

All metals with simple cubic crystal structures have at least five and, therefore, are capable of slip, whereas ceramics have fewer than five and are brittle. Von Mises also derived a mathematical method for checking whether slip systems are independent, but this takes us into the realms of crystal physics; we will stick with engineering here! ◁

In brittle materials, Stage I growth is unlikely because there are insufficient slip systems available to permit ductile deformation by dislocation movement. So, in ceramics, crack initiation is primarily from intrinsic processing defects such as porosity and grain-boundary flaws. Finishing marks, such as scratches and chipping due to machining, are also capable of creating stress concentrations sufficiently high to initiate cracks.

Because of the brittle nature of ceramics, you might think that fatigue would not occur in these materials. However, there is conclusive evidence of true, cyclic fatigue-crack growth in ceramics, although the mechanisms for fatigue-crack growth

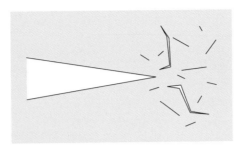

Figure 3.35 Microcracks developing ahead of the main crack can join and extend the length of the growing crack

in brittle materials are more complex than for those in a ductile material. One such mechanism is that crack growth occurs by accumulated damage from localized microplasticity and microcracking, particularly at grain boundaries, leading to crack advance, as illustrated in Figure 3.35.

One unusual aspect of slow crack growth in ceramics is that it can occur without the load being cycled. So, a crack in a ceramic material can grow slowly to failure even when the applied load is constant. This is known as *static fatigue*. The reason for this is attributed to environmental factors: slow chemical events at the crack tip that allow it to advance at a slow rate until eventually failure occurs.

SAQ 3.4 (Learning outcomes 3.3 and 3.4)

Outline briefly the mechanisms by which fatigue cracks grow in:

(a) metals

(b) polymers

(c) ceramics.

5 SUMMARY

This part has provided you with an overview of some of the mechanisms that underpin materials' behaviour, and in particular those mechanisms that can influence fatigue and fracture.

Most designers who select and apply materials for their properties may not need to know any detail of why a particular class of materials behaves in the way that it does. And exactly how the material fails may be unimportant if the part being designed is not safety-critical or is not expected to bear a load that could exceed a failure stress or toughness.

The mechanisms become important when trying to establish an overall understanding of when a material can be operated safely, and whether different materials can be used in equivalent ways, which is not always the case. The local heating effects at a crack tip in a polymer contribute to its fatigue behaviour in a way that isn't seen in metals, for example.

In the next part of this block we will look at how the environment in which a material operates can critically affect its ability to bear a load.

LEARNING OUTCOMES

After studying Block 2 Part 3 you should be able to do the following.

3.1 Recognize and describe ductile and brittle fractures.

3.2 Recognize and describe the features of a fatigue failure surface.

3.3 Describe the mechanisms that cause the initiation and growth of fatigue cracks in metallic materials.

3.4 Describe the mechanisms of fatigue-crack growth in non-metallic materials.

ANSWERS TO EXERCISES

EXERCISE 3.1

The scale marker in Figure 3.21 enables us to use a ruler to calculate the approximate striation spacing. By making several trial readings, I reckon there are about eight striations in 1 μm, giving a striation spacing of 0.125 μm – that is, a crack growth rate of 1.3×10^{-7} metres per cycle.

ANSWERS TO SELF-ASSESSMENT QUESTIONS

SAQ 3.1

The final fracture surface appears to be flat; it is shiny and at right angles to the axis of the specimen. This identifies it as a brittle fracture.

SAQ 3.2

(a) (i)   Fatigue involves localized plastic deformation in slip bands during each load cycle. This forms notch-like intrusions on the surface. At values of the stress amplitude above the fatigue limit, this plastic deformation eventually leads to the production of cracks within the slip bands.

   (ii)   During Stage I crack growth the crack continues to advance down the damaged slip band. In Stage II growth the crack leaves the slip band and turns to be perpendicular to the largest principal stress. Plastic flow still has a role because it is the means by which the fatigue crack advances and leaves striations in its wake.

(b)   If plastic deformation can be made more difficult, then the fatigue strength should be improved. At a given stress, less damage should be produced within slip bands and, hence, crack initiation should be deferred, giving a longer life.

   We have already seen that the fatigue limit tends to be a certain proportion of the material's yield strength. A higher yield strength means a higher fatigue limit.

SAQ 3.3

(a)   The fracture exhibits three distinct zones (Figure 3.36). The two zones that have started from the inner corners of the hub section are regions of fatigue-crack growth: both contain a series of 'beach marks' that represents the area of the growing crack. The zone between these two fatigue surfaces is the fast-fracture region, which would be the last to fail, where the cross section was no longer able to support the applied load.

fast-fracture region

initiation points

beach marks

Figure 3.36   Annotated version of Figure 3.23

(b) The crack has grown from the two corners of the inner edge, so this suggests that the hub was loaded in bending as the wheel rotated, thereby creating an alternating tension–compression cyclic loading.

SAQ 3.4

(a) In metals, crack growth proceeds by repeated plasticity at the crack tip. The cyclic loading advances the crack gradually each cycle, leaving a striation on the fracture surface.

(b) In polymers, fatigue occurs either by breaking cross-linked bonds at the tip of the crack (if the polymer is relatively brittle) or by local melting caused by viscoelastic heating.

(c) In ceramics, a 'damage zone' of microcracks forms ahead of the crack tip, and the crack can then grow forward into this region.

Ceramics can also show static fatigue, where a crack advances slowly even when the load is constant. This occurs by environmental attack of the highly stressed material at the crack tip.

ACKNOWLEDGEMENTS

Grateful acknowledgement is made to the following sources:

FIGURES

Figure 3.1: Reproduced by permission of IBM Research, Almaden Research Center. Unauthorized use not permitted.

Figure 3.3 (a) and (b): Courtesy of Tom Matthams, DoITPoMS project, Cambridge University.

Figure 3.12: Cotton, H.C. (1981) 'Experience in the petroleum industries', *Fracture mechanics in design and service: a Royal Society discussion*, The Royal Society.

Figure 3.13: Courtesy of Cranfield University.

Figure 3.20(b): Courtesy of Dr P. Forsyth, RAE Farnborough.

Figure 3.29: Beahan, P., Bevis, M. and Hull, D. (1975) 'Fracture processes in polystyrene', *Proceedings of The Royal Society*, vol. A343, © The Royal Society.

Figure 3.34(a): Courtesy of Ian Norman.

COURSE TEAM ACKNOWLEDGEMENTS

This part was prepared for the course team by Jim Moffatt.

CONTENTS

1 INTRODUCTION

Structures are not always doomed to fail, but they do usually have a limited useful life. Exceptions include many of the monuments that have survived from the ancient world, such as the Great Pyramid in Egypt (Figure 4.1a), the Pont du Gard in southern France (Figure 4.1b) and the Pantheon in Rome (Figure 4.1c). These are very stable structures. The Great Pyramid has a very low centre of gravity and few potential failure modes, while the other two structures are based on the principle of the arch and the dome respectively, where most of the loads in the stonework are compressive by nature, thereby exploiting the high compressive strength of stone. Stone is also very resistant to deterioration, particularly in relatively dry environments (which is why these structures have lasted so long).

In this part of the course we will examine some of the mechanisms of deterioration of structures, the effects of the way that structures are loaded on the process of degradation, and the ways structures can be protected against environmental attack. To help you to tackle the problems encountered by real structures in different

Figure 4.1 (a) The Great Pyramid, Giza; (b) Pont du Gard, France; (c) the Pantheon, Rome

environments, some background in the chemistry of materials will be provided to enable you to pinpoint specific mechanisms of deterioration.

This first section will introduce you to some of the language and mechanisms of corrosion and degradation. The remainder of this part uses a series of case studies to illustrate the various factors that can lead to failure in practice.

1.1 Degradation, dissolution and corrosion

A variety of common terms are used to describe the ways in which structural materials can be attacked by environments and although they do have specific connotations, they are frequently used as blanket terms for material deterioration. I shall attempt to define them in a more specific way, namely:

- Degradation: loss of strength of non-metals such as wood, rope or textile.

- Dissolution: removal of material in solution owing to the attacking medium.

- Corrosion: attack of metallic materials.

EXERCISE 4.1

Suggest appropriate terms for the following phenomena:

(a) rusting of a corrugated iron roof (Figure 4.2a)

(b) removal of limestone by rain water (Figure 4.2b)

(c) rotting of a timber beam (Figure 4.2c).

(a)

(c)

(b)

Figure 4.2   (a) Corrugated iron roof; (b) limestone gravestones; (c) rotten timber beams

When real products are examined in detail, one is forced to examine the many specific mechanisms by which they can deteriorate. Rusting, rotting and dissolution are very common in practical experience simply because of the widespread use of steel, limestone and timber in structures.

However, in order to study these (and other) mechanisms, we need to apply more rigorous analyses. The point of study is to design ways of eliminating deterioration, or at least (if attack is inevitable, as it often is in practice) ways of controlling and reducing the rate of attack. Most structures need to have a protracted life, not only to justify the expense of their erection, but also to protect the users. One of the unfortunate features of structural deterioration is the insidious way in which attack can occur, often hidden from view, and proceeding at a rate that can result in sudden and catastrophic failure of a safety-critical component. We shall be examining some examples later in this part.

1.2 Corrosion processes

For many materials, degradation processes are simply one or a series of chemical reactions that act to erode or deteriorate the material. The deterioration of metals is a little more complex than that of non-metals because metals are electrical conductors. Local ☑ **electrochemical cells** ☑ frequently form in the exposed surfaces of metals, leading to corrosion of the metal in one part of the cell. Electron movement is an essential part of the process: as electrons are lost, metal ions are formed, and these soluble metal ions then pass into the aqueous environment, resulting in a net loss of metal. Electrochemical cells were actually used by Volta to produce electricity (in the first batteries), so you can see that corrosion can be turned to advantage to make portable power sources.

☑ Electrochemical cells

The most familiar type of electrochemical cell to most people is the common battery. Batteries harness the energy released by corrosion of metal components, which is why they are usually heavy. An electrochemical cell contains two electrodes made from differing metals. When the terminals are connected, each electrode reacts with a current-carrying solution known as an electrolyte and the cell provides a current.

The two electrodes in any cell are known as the *cathode* and the *anode*. At the anode, the metal reacts and releases electrons. These electrons then flow through the connection to the cathode. We can write the anodic reaction in chemical shorthand as:

$$M \rightarrow M^+ + e^-$$

where M is a metal, and M^+ is a positively charged ion formed when the metal atom loses an electron e^-. Different metals will lose different numbers of electrons in a corrosion process. The resulting metal ion may be lost into a solution, or form part of a corrosion product such as rust. ▷

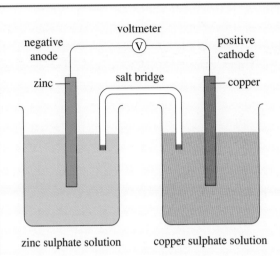

Figure 4.3   A Daniell cell

voltmeter

negative anode

positive cathode

zinc

salt bridge

copper

zinc sulphate solution   copper sulphate solution

At the cathode, the reverse reaction occurs. Electrons are 'absorbed' by ions, causing a different reaction, which might be the plating out of a metal from solution.

'Primary cells' are non-rechargeable: an example is the zinc–carbon battery, with a zinc anode and a carbon cathode that are separated by an electrolyte gel containing a salt (ammonium chloride). The electrolyte effectively attacks the zinc to produce electrons that can be tapped off at will. A *Daniell cell* uses copper and zinc as the electrodes, the copper being the cathode and the zinc the anode (Figure 4.3). Here the 'salt bridge' allows ions to travel between the two solutions, thus completing the circuit.

The life of every cell is limited by the amount of anode present, because this is attacked and effectively disappears, corroding away until little metal is left. So here is a possible tool to assess corrosive activity. Some metals are clearly more reactive than others; in other words, they have a greater electrical potential. It is possible to create a table that allows the electrical potentials of different metals to be compared. This may be done by putting two metals into a cell in order to determine which will corrode in preference to the other. Each specific cell has a characteristic *electromotive force* (emf), also known as the electrical potential difference, which is measured in volts. This shows how much more reactive one metal is than the other.

In order for all metals to be comparable, they must be measured against a standard point. Thus a 'hydrogen electrode' provides an arbitrary zero against which the other corrosion reactions are measured, to produce a list of standard electrode potentials (E^0) for different metals. This is shown in Table 4.1, and is known as the *electrochemical series*. The least reactive metals are at the top of the list; the most reactive are at the bottom. So, the more positive the standard electrode potential, the less likely a material is to corrode; the more negative the value, the more likely the material is to corrode. When two dissimilar metals are in contact, it will always be the metal with lower potential that corrodes.

Table 4.1   The electrochemical series

Electrode		Electrode reaction	E^0/V
Au	Gold	$Au^{3+} + 3e^- \rightleftharpoons Au$	+1.43
Ag	Silver	$Ag^+ + e^- \rightleftharpoons Ag$	+0.80
Cu	Copper	$Cu^{2+} + 2e^- \rightleftharpoons Cu$	+0.34
H	Hydrogen	$H^+ + e^- \rightleftharpoons H$	0
Pb	Lead	$Pb^{2+} + 2e^- \rightleftharpoons Pb$	−0.13
Sn	Tin	$Sn^{2+} + 2e^- \rightleftharpoons Sn$	−0.14
Ni	Nickel	$Ni^{2+} + 2e^- \rightleftharpoons Ni$	−0.25
Cd	Cadmium	$Cd^{2+} + 2e^- \rightleftharpoons Cd$	−0.40
Fe	Iron	$Fe^{2+} + 2e^- \rightleftharpoons Fe$	−0.44
Zn	Zinc	$Zn^{2+} + 2e^- \rightleftharpoons Zn$	−0.76
Ti	Titanium	$Ti^{2+} + 2e^- \rightleftharpoons Ti$	−1.63
Al	Aluminium	$Al^{3+} + 3e^- \rightleftharpoons Al$	−1.66
Mg	Magnesium	$Mg^{2+} + 2e^- \rightleftharpoons Mg$	−2.37
Na	Sodium	$Na^+ + e^- \rightleftharpoons Na$	−2.71
K	Potassium	$K^+ + e^- \rightleftharpoons K$	−2.93
Li	Lithium	$Li^+ + e^- \rightleftharpoons Li$	−3.05

1.2.1 Galvanic corrosion

When two dissimilar metals are in contact, or in close proximity with a conducting fluid in between, an electrochemical cell can be formed that leads to the more reactive metal becoming an anode and the less reactive metal a cathode.

This kind of corrosion is known as *galvanic corrosion*. It is not uncommon, since metals are often coated with others of different E^0, and different metals are often in close contact with a common electrolyte.

One of the earliest examples of galvanic corrosion was recorded in the eighteenth century. The wooden hull of the Royal Navy frigate HMS *Alarm* (Figure 4.4) had been covered by copper sheathing, which was attached to the hull by iron nails.

One of the purposes of the copper sheath was to limit marine biofouling, which is known to plague many materials that are immersed in sea water. The growth

Figure 4.4   HMS *Alarm*

of molluscs such as barnacles on the hulls of ships, which can then trap trailing seaweed, results in reduced speed and manoeuvrability. Copper limits fouling by inhibiting the attachment of molluscs. (Other organisms, such as bacteria, can also actually cause corrosion, as discussed in ◁ **Bacterial corrosion** ▷.)

◁ Bacterial corrosion

An unusual and perhaps unexpected corrosion problem can be caused by bacteria. As one of the oldest groups of organisms on the planet, bacteria have evolved to survive even in extreme environments. Bacterial corrosion can occur in fuel tanks, for example (Figure 4.5): fuel oil contaminates bilge water on tankers, and bacteria then grow profusely in the mixture.

The bacteria feed on the organic oil, releasing mild organic acids and depleting the oxygen content of the water. The acids will accelerate corrosion of the steel container, but a more serious stage can develop when certain species known as sulphate-reducing bacteria take over. These reduce the oxygen content of the sulphates commonly present in dirty fuel oils to produce hydrogen sulphide, or H_2S. This compound is potent at corroding steel and can also enhance hydrogen embrittlement (which is a form of stress corrosion cracking), attack usually occurring as pits in the metal close to or under the bacterial colonies. Such colonies are perhaps better known for the 'rusticles' they produce – as were present on the wreck of the *Titanic* (Figure 4.6). The colonies of bacteria live on the rust, and promote further rusting through chemical attack of the underlying steel.

Figure 4.5   Colonies of bacteria in the bottom of a fuel tank

Such bacterial attack can also cause disasters directly, as in the gas explosion near Carlsbad in New Mexico, USA on 19 August 2000. The natural gas was carried in a 760 mm diameter steel pipe across a river via a suspension bridge. The pipe fractured suddenly, releasing gas that ignited into a fireball, engulfing the bridge and killing 12 people. It left a large crater, at the base of which were found the ends ▷

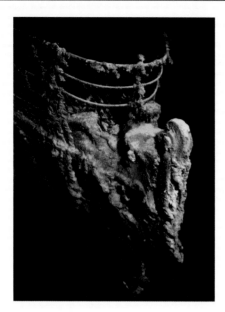

Figure 4.6 Rusticles on the bow of the *Titanic*

of the pipe; the missing pieces were ejected by the explosion (Figure 4.7).

Analysis of sludge found in the pipe showed evidence of extensive microbial attack in the form of deep pits in the pipe wall, and the presence of various contaminants including chlorides, hydrogen sulphide and sulphates. The fracture had occurred at a deeply corroded section of the 7.6 mm thick wall, where the wall thickness had been reduced to less than 2.5 mm. The rupture took the form of a 525 mm long crack along the axis of the pipe, which was under an internal pressure of 4.65 MPa. Better inspection procedures were recommended after the accident, including the use of cleaning 'pigs', which travel within pipes, both monitoring internal problems and cleaning debris away.

EXERCISE 4.2

Calculate the approximate hoop stress in the pipe assuming no wall thinning, and then the effect of microbial corrosion on the hoop stress when the wall thickness has reduced to 2.5 mm.

You should recall that the hoop stress in a cylinder is given by:

$$\sigma_h = \frac{pr}{t_c}$$

Figure 4.7 Crater formed by gas explosion: the missing length of pipe (between the two arrows) was ejected

The hull was covered in 1761, and the copper sheath was found to be detached two years after fitting, during which time the *Alarm* had visited the Caribbean and elsewhere. The iron nails were found mostly to have corroded. Some nails remained intact, however, where their brown paper wrapping had remained in place between the

Figure 4.8   The Statue of Liberty

Polytetrafluoroethylene (PTFE) is a synthetic polymer that has an extremely low coefficient of friction and is very non-reactive.

---

copper and the iron, a fortuitous event that prevented total detachment of the sheath. The iron nails in contact with the copper were subject to rapid galvanic corrosion that led to detachment of the sheathing. The small anode (iron nails) to cathode (copper sheet) area ratio favoured the loss of the iron, as the rate of corrosion is directly proportional to the current density (a measure of electron flow). In a sense, the nails acted as local electron concentrators, so attack was rapid. Where it was present, the brown paper insulated the nails and so there was insufficient electron flow to cause corrosion.

The reason why marine environments are especially pernicious is the salt content of sea water. The presence of sodium and chloride ions increases the electrical conductivity compared with pure water, so galvanic or other cells formed between dissimilar metals react much faster.

Another example of a structure that was damaged by galvanic corrosion was the Statue of Liberty in New York harbour (Figure 4.8). Built in 1886 by Gustav Eiffel and Frederic Bartholdi, it was composed of an inner wrought-iron framework, with an outer cladding of copper attached by saddles of copper.

The risk of galvanic corrosion had been anticipated and so the two metals were separated by asbestos and shellac insulation. (Shellac is a natural resin that was widely used in the Victorian period as a lacquer or protective coating.) However, the shellac had degraded, and acidic rainwater had soaked the insulation, providing electrolytic conduction between the metals. The corrosion of the iron framework (Figure 4.9) was so extensive that there was concern it might collapse, and so in 1986 the statue was renovated. The wrought-iron framework was replaced by stainless steel, which will not corrode in the presence of copper, coated in a layer of PTFE insulation.

Highly localized attack, such as that found on the Statue, is also known as *crevice corrosion*, because attack is concentrated in the contact zone at the junction of the two dissimilar metals. A crevice forms and further attack occurs there, making the hole deeper (Figure 4.10). It is a common feature of corrosion, and can be contrasted with general overall attack. It is that much more dangerous since the damage is

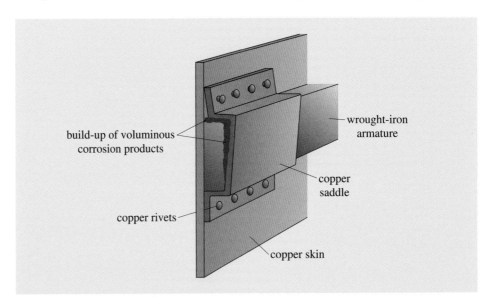

Figure 4.9   Galvanic corrosion on the Statue of Liberty

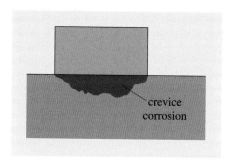

Figure 4.10   Crevice corrosion

usually hidden from external inspection, until the strength of a product is reduced to a critical level and it fractures through the crevice. The loss of material lowers the section area, and there may also be a stress concentration within the crevice to magnify the stress further. Where the load levels are low, as in a galvanized water tank, nothing will happen until it leaks and alerts the owner to the problem. However, where a pressurized tank such as a boiler suffers the same problem, the effects may be much more dramatic.

EXERCISE 4.3

Suggest why the rate of corrosion was lower on the Statue of Liberty than on HMS *Alarm*.

SAQ 4.1 (Learning outcomes 4.4 and 4.5)

Explain the following observations of corrosion in terms of the electrochemical series:

(a) An empty, tin-plated steel food can will rust very rapidly after use if left outside.

(b) When the zinc coating on galvanized steel is broken, the underlying steel will rust only slowly.

1.2.2 Galvanic series

A similar concept to the electrochemical series that has been used by engineers for many years is the *galvanic series* (one example of which is shown in Table 4.2: here the list should be read down the columns rather than across the rows). It ranks metals and alloys in order of reactivity or electrical potential, just like the electrochemical series. It also has the same properties: the greater the difference in position between two metals or alloys, the greater the likelihood that corrosion will occur. The series differs from the electrochemical series in showing alloys, which are of course of direct practical interest. Closely related alloys such as the brasses and bronzes are grouped together. Again, the most reactive materials are towards the bottom of the list.

However, such lists must be used with caution because they are highly dependent on the actual conditions. Also, the numerical values associated with the electrochemical series can allow more accurate information to be gathered about likely corrosion rates.

Table 4.2   Galvanic series of some commercial metals and alloys in sea water

Gold	Tin
Graphite	Lead
Titanium	'Active' stainless steel (unstable oxide film)
'Passive' stainless steel (stable oxide film)	Cast iron and 'mild' steel
Silver	Cadmium
Nickel	Aluminium
Copper	Zinc
Bronze (Cu–Sn)	Magnesium and magnesium alloys
Brass (Cu–Zn)	

EXERCISE 4.4

Using first the galvanic series, then checking with the electrochemical series, suggest which pair of alloys below will show the greater tendency to corrode in a marine environment, if the exposed areas of the two components are roughly equal:

- mild steel and bronze
- magnesium alloy and steel.

1.3 Corrosion in stressed products – stress corrosion cracking (SCC)

If a stress exists in a product exposed to a corrosive environment, the rate of corrosion can then increase and be extremely localized, such as at the tip of a growing crack. Furthermore, some specific chemicals are so aggressive that corrosion will occur at relatively low stress levels, such as those created during manufacture, for example. The residual stress in a component can then be enough to trigger crack growth and failure.

1.3.1 Stress corrosion cracking in stainless-steel structures

On 9 May 1985 the roof of a swimming pool at Uster near Zurich collapsed, killing 12 and injuring several others.

The concrete roof had been held up by a set of stainless-steel tie bars, which were found after the accident to have cracked transversely (Figure 4.11). Chlorine is added at quite high levels to swimming-pool water supplies in order to control bacterial contamination from swimmers. It is a very powerful oxidizing agent, and can attack a very wide range of materials, typically by forming hairline cracks in components that are in tension. Traces of chlorine gas in the general atmosphere of the building

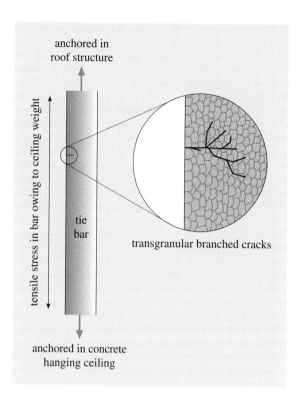

anchored in
roof structure

tensile stress in bar owing to ceiling weight

tie
bar

transgranular branched cracks

anchored in concrete
hanging ceiling

Figure 4.11   Transverse cracking in stainless-steel tie bars

were found to be the cause, having attacked the material chemically. Stainless steel and many other types of steel are known to be susceptible to chlorine attack, as are certain plastic materials.

After that tragedy, yet further failures occurred in swimming pools. In the Netherlands, for example, a ceiling collapsed during the night of 8/9 June 2001 at a pool in Stenwijk. It was discovered the next morning by a party of visiting swimmers; fortunately there were no casualties. The pool had been open only nine years, and chlorine was again used to disinfect the water of the pool. The design of this swimming pool was slightly different, however. The ceiling above the pool was reasonably well supported, but there were air ducts above weighing several hundred kilograms. These were attached to the outer roof above by stainless-steel threaded bars. Upon examination, the threads were found to be deeply cracked. When the cracks reached a critical size, the air ducts fell onto the ceiling, which in turn failed owing to the extra load and the shock, or impact, loading.

Stainless steel is used extensively in swimming-pool fixtures such as handrails, ladders leading from the pool and diving boards. It has been found to perform well, without cracking, for many years, even with constant immersion in warm water dosed with low levels of chlorine. The metal has a polished surface and so can be cleaned easily, and would normally have a long and uneventful life. But the stresses applied in these fixtures are only intermittent, not continuous. Except perhaps for diving boards, the fittings are over-designed, so the imposed loads from the users are relatively low.

However, when similar grades of stainless steel are used as tie bars, they are under continuous tension, which is when stress corrosion cracking becomes a relevant failure mode. The air circulating in the ducts above the Stenwijk pool will have been

Falling objects will impose much greater loads than their nominal weight owing to the momentum gained by the drop. The exact force of the impact will depend on the distance through which they fall.

saturated with water vapour as well as carrying traces of free chlorine gas, and will have attacked the protective oxide film on the steel. This attack will have produced brittle cracks, which then grew slowly under the tensile load, with new metal being exposed as the crack advanced. The high stress concentration at the advancing crack tip, together with the imposed tensile load, will have encouraged further crack growth until criticality.

EXERCISE 4.5

Explain why the cracks were initiated at the roots of the threads.

Even low tensile loads will have been enough to stimulate crack initiation, owing to the importance of stress concentrations in magnifying the imposed load. The critical threshold for the initiation of SCC is normally very low, but must be a *tensile* stress. The other interesting feature of these failures is the continued attack by very low levels of gaseous chlorine. The chlorine levels are lower than in the pool water, so the extent of the attack probably relates to the much greater ease with which gas molecules can penetrate a corrosion film.

The incident in the Netherlands led to a survey of several thousand swimming pools in the country. It emerged that 14 pools were at immediate risk of sudden failure owing to deeply cracked suspension bolts of a similar design to those at the original pool. They were closed immediately for repair. A further 18 pools were considered dangerous and needed extra support of the ducting. Most of the pools were very new, one being only a year old. The stainless-steel parts were replaced with galvanized steel equivalents or with stainless steel with a high molybdenum content (~6%), both of which are much more resistant to SCC.

The accident led to other surveys in Germany and the UK, where a warning notice was circulated by the Health and Safety Executive. It highlights the dangers arising from using what appear to be corrosion-resistant materials in situations where brittle cracks can develop quickly in safety-critical components.

Stainless steel is also sensitive to chloride ions (such as those present in sea water and brine), and especial care is needed in designing the material for use in ships and boats where exposure can occur.

1.3.2 Cracking of copper alloys

Stainless steel is not the only metal to fall victim to SCC. One of the first discoveries of SCC occurred in India in the early part of the nineteenth century, when that country was still part of the British Empire. There was a large standing army that was always in need of live ammunition. The brass cartridge cases would occasionally split, and often at the worst possible time (when being fired), frequently causing injury to the marksman.

So what caused such failures? The two factors needed for stress corrosion cracks are, first, a tensile stress in the outer layers of the brass and, second, an active chemical that will attack brass or copper. The stress could be caused by the manufacturing forces used to shape the cartridges, since the cases were made from cold-deformed

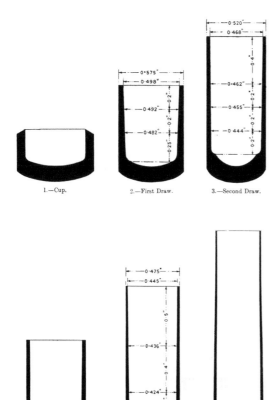

Figure 4.12 Process used to make cartridges

brass (70% copper, 30% zinc). The process involved successive stages of deformation of flat discs punched out from 3.25 mm thick sheet (Figure 4.12). After each stage, the product was annealed in order to recrystallize the metal, and pickled with sulphuric acid to remove oxide at the surface. The annealing process was intended to relieve residual stresses set up in the cases, but the process was not always successful in completely removing these stresses.

After some detective work, an association was seen between the rate of cracking and the season of the year. Cracking tended to occur during the monsoon season when humidity and temperatures were high, rather than during the cooler months. Yet although the rate of most chemical reactions increases with temperature, controlled experiments showed that this could not have been the only cause of the problem. Then the Woolwich Arsenal undertook a series of trials with many different chemicals. They exposed bent strips of brass to the chemicals and observed the metal surfaces at the most highly stressed zones. They found that ammonia gas and water vapour were, in combination, the two most potent agents needed to initiate brittle cracks. Bearing in mind the experience of stainless steel in chlorine-doped water, it is interesting that failure times for many samples dipped into ammonia solutions were longer than for exposure to ammonia gas and water vapour.

The mystery was therefore solved, because it was realized that ammonia is produced by manure and dung, so would have been present in the stables of the army horses, for example. If ammunition had been stored near the stables, it is most likely that trace amounts of ammonia in humid air could have cracked the brass cases extremely quickly. Hairline or microscopic cracks would have been formed, and then grown to a critical size by the time the ammunition was needed.

So why does cracking or highly localized attack occur in such a case, rather than general corrosion? The active agents attack at stress raisers, at the upper edge where the case makes contact with the bullet (Figure 4.13). The formation of a galvanic cell is unlikely, because a thin film of water on the surface is insufficient to provide the electrolyte. However, the final stage of manufacture, when the bullet is put in the explosive-filled case, will put the lip under a radial or hoop stress. The edge is unlikely to be totally level, and small degrees of roughness there will be attacked by the ammonia. Once a crack has formed, it will grow under the influence of the hoop stress, with the corrosive solution seeping away to leave a fresh crack tip ready for further attack.

The problem of chemical attack on brass and other copper alloys is not uncommon, as the example described in ☑ **Pump failures** ☑ demonstrates.

Figure 4.13   Stress corrosion cracks on brass cartridges

☑ Pump failures

Brittle ceramic products are frequently impregnated with softer and tougher materials to strengthen them. Ceramics usually have an open pore structure, and filling the pores with a crack-resistant material toughens the final product. Such a process is used to improve the toughness of anodes used for the electrolytic production of aluminium, and involves applying a vacuum to a chamber in which the anodes are placed. Liquid pitch is then pumped into the chamber to fill the pores, before the anodes are removed for baking so as to solidify the pitch.

After six months' operation, the vacuum in one such chamber deteriorated and investigation pointed to failure of an impellor used to apply the vacuum. The impellor was made from brass and had suffered severe corrosion, with the formation of a green deposit over all the surfaces (Figure 4.14). The impellor was replaced, but the vacuum again began to deteriorate. The time had come to perform a serious investigation, especially as the impellors were rather expensive.

Suspicion fell on the liquid pitch, as it had a high sulphur content, but an alternative explanation quickly became apparent. Several operators had smelled ammonia in the pitch, but it took an alert manager to recognize the cause of the corrosion. As an OU student studying forensic engineering, he correctly identified that the ammonia had attacked the copper component of the brass to form cuprammonium salts, attack being most severe at the tips of the flight vanes and corners of the design where the local stresses were highest. ▷

Figure 4.14   Green deposit on the surface of the corroded impellor

At these points, stress corrosion cracking had further weakened the impellor. The net result was loss of material leading to loss of evacuation power, with a lower vacuum for impregnation.

So what was the solution to the problem? One possibility was to replace the rotor with stainless steel, but this was an expensive option. A lower-cost solution would be to apply a resistant coating to the surface of existing brass impellors, which would prevent the ammonia contacting the brass surfaces. Several different polymer coatings could be used, such as sintering powdered PVC or polypropylene onto the part, but the final solution involved using epoxy resin. The pumps have, since this innovation, proved entirely trouble-free.

1.3.3 Boiler explosions

Stress corrosion cracks can also build up in other structures. These were a particular problem in locomotive boilers in the early days of the railways in Britain. All such boilers were made from wrought-iron sheet, riveted together to form a cylinder. In the earliest engines, the boilers were constructed using a single line of rivets, thus forming two corners, one inside and the other outside (Figure 4.15). Initially they apparently performed well, but a number of catastrophic explosions were experienced through the 1840s.

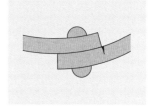

Figure 4.15   Riveted joint between two wrought-iron sheets in boiler construction

Some of the earliest explosions were caused by failures of the safety valves fitted to the boilers. For example, some of the first safety valves were simply a stopcock weighed down by a steelyard. The weight and its distance along the arm controlled the pressure at which steam would activate the cock, and so blow off harmlessly. It was tempting for engine drivers to increase boiler pressure by adjusting to the highest possible pressure – and if that didn't give enough driving power to the wheels, they would wedge the valve down further. Such manipulation of a safety device was asking for trouble. Another problem that also caused some explosions was that if the water level dropped too far, the structure would overheat and fail.

Many such boiler explosions were investigated by the Railway Inspectors appointed by the Board of Trade (one of the predecessors of the Department of Trade and Industry). They found that they could not always explain why the explosions had occurred, having excluded both human negligence in the use of the safety valves and the water level. When the inspectors examined the failed remains in some detail, they found a pattern revealing that failure almost always occurred from the horizontal line of rivets in the boiler, and there appeared to be a deep groove running alongside the joint that was filled with rust.

SAQ 4.2 (Learning outcome 4.6)

Explain why failure tended to occur along the longitudinal axis of the boiler, using the concepts of the stress in a cylindrical pressure vessel from Block 1 Part 4.

Why would a riveted joint represent a line of weakness? How could such a joint be strengthened?

The root cause of the problem lay in corrosive attack of the wall to one side of the joint, owing to the nature of the joint itself. The wall on either side would, when the pressure was being raised first thing in the morning, experience higher stress than the double wall thickness at the joint itself, owing to the existence of a corner where the plates met acting as a stress raiser. Corrosion of the iron by the boiler water tended to start here in the form of a slowly growing crack, a process repeated every morning the locomotive was worked. The cycling of hoop stress caused whenever steam was raised and the boiler pressurized could also have given rise to fatigue cracking, although the phenomenon was not recognized as such at the time.

The purity of the boiler water would be important in such a case, because if any dissolved salts were present they would increase its electrical conductivity and hence the likelihood of corrosion cells being set up near the joint.

Such 'groove cracking' was a design fault, which could be corrected only by developing a double-riveted butt joint (as shown in the answer to SAQ 4.2) in place of the lap joint, rigorous inspection and maintenance of locomotives and, ultimately, use of stronger steel in place of the wrought iron.

2 CASE STUDY 1: THE SILVER BRIDGE

Stress corrosion cracking can produce devastating damage in large structures, as the examples of swimming-pool ceilings and roofs in Section 1 showed. But even larger structures can also be attacked, as was revealed by the events at the Silver Bridge in 1967.

DVD

The Silver Bridge spanned the Ohio river between West Virginia and Ohio. It was a long bridge (680 m), owing to the breadth of the river at Point Pleasant, the small settlement on the east bank where one end was sited. It was nearly 12 metres wide in total, carrying a concrete road two lanes in width as well as a footpath. It had been built in 1928 alongside an older railway bridge, but to a strikingly different design (Figure 4.16).

It was effectively a suspension bridge, but one that used eye bars and rigid hangers to support the deck, rather than the familiar steel cables of modern suspension bridges. The main chain system was not unlike a bicycle chain, each structural unit being a set of steel links held together laterally on a pin (Figure 4.17). Such a design had been used previously on the Brighton chain pier, Telford's Menai Straits bridge and

This case study is illustrated further by the programme on the DVD called 'The Silver Bridge disaster and its legacy'. You should watch this programme alongside the case study, as you will find it easier to tackle the associated SAQs.

Figure 4.16   The Silver Bridge (left)

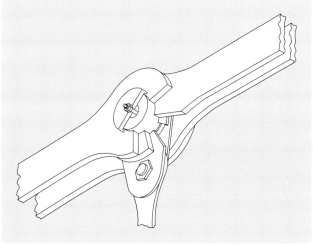

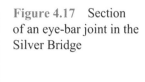

Figure 4.17   Section of an eye-bar joint in the Silver Bridge

Brunel's Clifton bridge in the Victorian period, although in those cases the links were generally made of three or more bars, rather than just two. The Clifton bridge possessed no fewer than six such bars strapped together.

There had previously been problems with suspension bridge roadways that were too flexible, and several bridges had been severely damaged, if not destroyed, by lateral winds: see ☑ **Historic suspension bridge failures** ☑.

☑ Historic suspension bridge failures

Failures of suspension bridges (see Table 4.3) have most frequently involved failure of the suspended deck rather than of the support structure. A famous early failure occurred in the Brighton chain pier in 1836, when a storm destroyed the deck (Figure 4.18). Built in 1822, the pier was 352 m long and 3.9 m wide. Five cast-iron towers, spaced 78 m apart, supported the decks. The pier, which served for embarkation of new ferry services to France after the Napoleonic wars, was damaged many times by storms and then rebuilt, until it was finally demolished in 1896.

Figure 4.18   Brighton chain pier after storm damage in 1836

Table 4.3 Suspension bridge failures

Bridge	Location	Year of failure	Main span/m	Width of deck/m	Designer
Dryburgh Abbey	Scotland	1818	79	1.2	J. and W. Smith
Nassau	Germany	1834	75	–	Lossen and Wolf
Brighton Chain Pier	England	1836	78	3.9	Samuel Brown
Montrose	Scotland	1838	132	7.9	Samuel Brown
Menai Straits	Wales	1839	177	7.3	Thomas Telford
Angers	France	1850	110	8.0	Joseph Chaley
Roche-Bernard	Scotland	1852	79	1.2	J. and W. Smith
Wheeling	USA	1854	309	7.3	Charles Ellet
Lewiston-Queenston	USA	1864	318	5.9	Edward Serrell
Niagara-Clifton	USA	1889	386	5.2	Samuel Keefer
Tacoma Narrows	USA	1940	854	11.9	Leon Moisseiff

Perhaps more famous was the bridge built by Thomas Telford over the Menai Straits in 1826 (the deck of which was also damaged severely on several occasions, especially in 1839). The Angers disaster in France was the most serious failure, since 226 soldiers were killed when the bridge fell. Corrosion of the anchors of the main cables was one cause of the disaster.

The Clifton suspension bridge was built to a design by Isambard Kingdom Brunel, but was not completed until 1864, after his death. Despite having been damaged in the past, the Menai Straits and Clifton bridges still stand today. Both use many eye-bar chains to support the deck, giving high redundancy if one fails. However, many other suspension bridges failed as designers produced longer and longer decks, culminating in the famous collapse of the bridge over the Tacoma Narrows.

 DVD

The Tacoma Narrows bridge failure can be seen in 'The riddle of the Tay Bridge disaster' on the course DVD.

The Tacoma bridge was completely wrecked in 1940 (although the towers and main cables remained intact). The failure occurred through dynamic stimulus of the very long deck by a steady wind of approximately 40 mph blowing at right angles to the axis of the deck. But rather than oscillating from side to side, it started rolling up and down as it resonated. The amplitude rose steadily until failure of the deck occurred, and then other parts followed (Figure 4.19). The accident was the culmination of a sequence of similar incidents in which sub-critical oscillations occurred (which gave the bridge the nickname 'Galloping Gertie'). The failure highlighted the problem of the effect of winds on very large structures. Large buildings, such as skyscrapers, routinely have giant pistons fitted within to damp movements caused by high winds.

Figure 4.19 Sagging of approach at the Tacoma bridge after fall of centre deck, showing intact main cables

In the Silver Bridge there was a small clearance of about 3 mm between the pins and eye-bar holes, to allow easy fitting of the parts together when on site. The links were made from a high-strength steel that had been developed in the 1920s by the American Bridge Company. The eye bars had been cast to shape and then heat treated to develop the strength of the steel; then the holes were drilled out.

The roadway of the bridge was trussed with steel girders to improve its rigidity. There were two separate towers supporting the main suspension chains, each 40 m high; each tower consisted of four tiers that were cross-braced except for the road gap (Figure 4.20). The towers were supported on two massive masonry piers anchored in the river bed, and the two sides supported by two further piers, one in the river bed and the other on land on the Ohio side of the river.

The main suspension chains were anchored in concrete troughs on each bank, each trough being pinned by 405 concrete piles to resist the tension exerted by the main chains. Each of the two towers was designed to move with temperature fluctuations in the chains by having curved rocker joints at its base on the masonry piers.

Figure 4.20 Tower of Silver Bridge

The bridge was inspected in 1954 and remedial work on decaying concrete recommended, together with painting of the metalwork. It was inspected again (after the remedial work had been finished) in 1955, 1961 and 1965.

SAQ 4.3 (Learning outcome 4.7)

Describe the types of load carried by:

(a) the towers

(b) the roadway

(c) each eye-bar link

(d) the pin through each joint.

Assuming that there was no traffic on the bridge, and no other external loading, where in the bridge were the eye-bar joints likely to be under the greatest load?

The bridge appeared to fulfil its function well, despite the loading on the bridge increasing steadily after it was built with the increase in car population and road traffic. The bridge had been built at a time when the Model T Ford was the most popular automobile on the roads, but by the 1960s cars were significantly larger and heavier, further increasing the load on the bridge.

Corrosion of the steel structure of the Silver Bridge was likely, especially as the acidity of the rain was enhanced locally by industry nearby. So the entire structure was painted with an aluminium-based paint, hence the name 'silver' bridge. An example of how corrosion can lead to failure of a bridge structure is described in ▽ **Fall of the Kinzua Viaduct** ▽.

▽ Fall of the Kinzua Viaduct

Many historic bridges and viaducts show the effects of long-term corrosion, which can often lead to catastrophic failure. Such a failure happened to the Kinzua Viaduct during the passage of a large storm through western Pennsylvania in July 2003. The Kinzua Viaduct had been built from cast and wrought iron by the New York, Lake Erie and Western Railroad Company in 1882 to deliver coal from local coalfields to the Great Lakes. It was reconstructed in steel in 1900 (Figure 4.21) to allow for the greater loads on the structure.

The viaduct was retired from active service in 1959, but the structure remained as the centrepiece of a national park, taking occasional traffic from sightseeing tours. However, the bridge required extensive renovation owing to rusting and was closed again to traffic. Renovation was started in February 2003, but on 21 July 2003 an unusually severe storm hit the region. During the storm, 11 of the viaduct's 20 towers fell, destroying the landmark (Figure 4.22).

Forensic investigation of the fall showed that the centre of the structure had oscillated from side to side as two tornados (with wind speeds of about 100 mph) struck the site. It was estimated that about four complete cycles occurred before its collapse.

Final failure had occurred at the rusted base bolts holding the structure to the foundations, which had fatigue cracked over a long period of time (Figure 4.23), assisted by internal rusting.

The lattice superstructure fell in several parts, the railway line ending up hundreds of feet away. The failure bears some similarity to the classic fall of the Tay Bridge in a severe storm in 1879, the main difference lying in the way the joints in the

DVD

The Kinzua bridge collapse is covered in the 'Kinzua's weakest link' programme on the course DVD.

Figure 4.21   Kinzua Viaduct with reconstruction in progress

Figure 4.22   Aerial view of the collapse

Figure 4.23   Cracked base-bolt shroud

structure behaved. Most of the cast-iron joints of the Tay Bridge failed either before or during the fall, so the railway line ended up close to the foundations. The steel joints at Kinzua remained mostly intact.

DVD

The fall of the Tay Bridge is covered in 'The riddle of the Tay Bridge disaster' on the course DVD.

2.1 The disaster

The 39-year-old Silver Bridge collapsed suddenly at about 5 p.m. on 15 December 1967 when the roadway was filled with rush-hour traffic – 37 vehicles were trapped on the roadway.

The first signs of collapse were later recounted by the survivors. Many occupants of the cars on the bridge had felt it 'quivering' before it fell. Most witnesses had then heard 'cracking' or 'popping' noises, some saying that it sounded like a 'shotgun blast'. After this, the bridge started disintegrating fast; girders and hangers fell, followed by collapse of the roadway itself near the centre of the bridge. The towers then fell, bringing the rest of the chains with them. The entire structure collapsed within about a minute, disgorging 31 of the 37 vehicles into the river below. Witnesses on the banks described the bridge falling like 'a house of cards', but many tried to save those who had escaped from their vehicles. Those who were trapped inside their sinking vehicles had little chance of escape, however, given that the river reached a depth of 20 m near the centre. Some broke their vehicle windows and managed to escape their sinking or sunken cars, swimming to the surface. The fall from the road deck and impact with the water rendered many of the victims unconscious and they drowned, trapped in their sunken vehicles. The temperature was about −1 °C, and the cold water of the river meant that anyone who survived the fall itself succumbed quickly to hypothermia. Despite heroic rescue attempts from both sides of the river, the disaster claimed 46 victims, although remarkably, three people from the centre section survived.

Recovery of the bodies took some time, and they were the first priority after all the swimming or stranded victims were rescued. However, it was vital to determine the cause of the accident, so the river bed was trawled thoroughly for all the metalwork that had fallen. Since virtually the whole bridge had disappeared (apart from the road deck on the West Virginia bank), this was a big job involving many weeks' work. It was difficult work as well, because the river was deep and fast-flowing at that point, as well as being very cold.

Although there had been many other bridge collapses in the USA before 1967, only one had been worse: the collapse of a railway truss bridge in 1876 at Ashtabula, in which over 100 died. For such a total collapse to have occurred in 1967 seemed unthinkable, given the progress in analytical design, the greater understanding of loading and the improvement in construction materials that had occurred since the 1920s.

A thorough and intensive investigation was needed to establish just what had happened to cause such a catastrophic failure. Several US government agencies were involved, including the National Transportation Safety Board (NTSB) and the National Standards Bureau (NSB), as well as the Battelle Memorial Institute and several university engineering departments.

2.2 The investigation

The investigation took three years to complete, although critical evidence emerged within weeks of the accident.

Some possibilities could be ruled out immediately. For example, there were rumours of supernatural forces at work that night, but very little solid evidence of the 'Mothman' emerged, either there or anywhere else. The Mothman was a demon purportedly haunting the bridge, which has supposedly appeared as a portent of similar disasters around the world. Such stories would have encouraged the investigators to speed their work so as to reassure the public that there were more rational causes of the bridge's fall.

2.2.1 Sequence of events

It was important to establish the precise sequence of events leading up to and during the collapse. From which part had the collapse started? Why had so much of the structure been destroyed? Was there any prior warning of the failure? What part had the weather conditions at the time played?

Eyewitnesses were plentiful, and each had a different perspective of the bridge as it fell. There were some common parts to their statements. Most of the witnesses, especially survivors from vehicles on the bridge at the time, testified that they heard cracking sounds very early in the collapse. This suggested that brittle fracture was an important failure mode, if not initiating the fall then certainly playing a crucial role in the disaster.

Testimony showed that the bridge vibrated during high lateral winds, and also when traffic crossed, which meant that movement in the eye-bar joints would have been occurring quite regularly. There was generally significant traffic across the bridge since it carried an Interstate highway.

Witness statements attested to unusual vibrations in the roadway just before the collapse. They also noticed that a bolt or cap-like object was seen on the roadway prior to or during the initial period of the collapse.

2.2.2 Planning the investigation

A plan was needed to determine the chain of events leading up to and during the collapse. That sequence would necessarily depend on which parts had broken first, and a fault tree would enable a plan of action in isolating the cause (or causes) of the disaster. Such a systematic approach is known as fault-tree analysis or FTA, and is part of the armoury of methods used by accident investigators. With large-scale and devastating accidents, all possibilities, however remote, need evaluation in the light of all the available evidence. In this way, the list can be whittled down to the vital one or small handful of most probable causes. Such a systematic approach is vital where both the material and the witness evidence is extensive, not just for the analysis of bridge or building failures where destruction is almost complete, but also for marine and aerospace disasters.

One action that was taken almost immediately was to close a bridge of very similar design some miles upstream, at St Mary's. That bridge would not just be subject to rigorous inspection but would also become the basis for experimental work on its dynamic behaviour when loaded under controlled conditions.

The possibility of wind action could also be ruled out, because the wind at the time of the accident was parallel to the long axis of the bridge, and was only about 6 mph. Likewise, there was no evidence that the masonry piers were involved. Indeed, they survived almost unscathed (Figure 4.24).

Figure 4.24   Masonry piers after the disaster

2.2.3 Reassembling the parts

As the wreckage was pulled from the river it was examined and identified, and any failures of the metal components were recognized and tagged. This was a mammoth task, given that virtually the whole bridge had fallen into the water, including all the road decks, trusses, chains and hangers, eye bars and the two towers. The parts were then reassembled and all the failed or fractured components photographed and catalogued. Over 90% of the bridge components were collected together and reorganized into their original positions in the bridge. Their position on the river bed before extraction was also an important facet of the investigation. To help reconstruct the sequence of events, the metal parts were classified into different categories:

- undamaged, or minimum damage

- ductile damage, such as distortion or bending

- separation of parts by fracture.

The fractured parts were then examined in detail to identify the extent of plasticity, exposure of fracture surfaces, and their chemical state.

Distinguishing the different kinds of damage to the many different structures in the bridge was time-consuming, and often difficult. Metal surfaces exposed by fracture would have rusted both in the river and later, when exposed to the atmosphere during storage and reassembly. A selection of critical failed parts needed to be identified for shipping to the many labs involved in detailed analysis of the components.

2.2.4 Examining the parts

Brittle fractures were discovered quickly in the mass of debris hauled from the river. Such samples became the focus of increasing effort as time went by, simply because they were unexpected. So the possible failure mechanisms were immediately narrowed down when brittle fractures of critical components started to emerge from the river.

SAQ 4.4 (Learning outcome 4.9)

Suggest what mechanisms could cause brittle fracture of steel components that might normally be expected to fail in a ductile manner.

2.3 Analysis of eye bar 330

One particular broken part was recognized quickly as part of an eye bar. There were 146 eye bars in the original bridge, and they were safety-critical because if broken the main chains could be threatened. The eye bar was identified as being from the top joint in the hanging chain nearest the bank and next to the Ohio tower, one of the two lower bars on the outside of the bridge facing north, upriver (Figure 4.25). It was assigned the identity number 330. It was 17 m long, 51 mm thick with a shank width of 305 mm. The hole in the end, designed to fit over the pin, was 368 mm in diameter, and the width of each limb beside the hole was about 203 mm (Figure 4.26).

Figure 4.25 Critical eye-bar joint on Ohio section of bridge

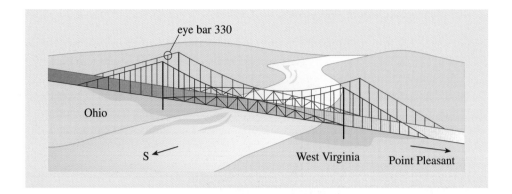

Figure 4.26 Structure of critical eye-bar joint

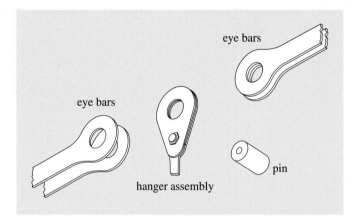

2.3.1 Fracture surface

One half of the eye at the joint is shown in Figure 4.27(a), and it shows two breaks in the limbs either side of the pin-hole. Although both appear brittle in this picture, in fact one side showed signs of ductile deformation. The way it had fractured was unique when compared with the other eye bars collected. The missing part of the eye bar was located and examined (Figure 4.27b). It corresponded well to the main part, although it had been damaged in one corner – presumably when it fell off the pin and impacted with the deck or another part of the bridge, which must have been still standing at that point in time. This second part shows more clearly the ductile portion on the left, where the limb has broken with a large lip projecting from one side of the component. This surface is seen in oblique view in Figure 4.27(c), a view that also shows a secondary crack or branch away from the main path of the crack. The surface on this ductile part of the eye bar was much coarser than the brittle fracture side. A thin layer of rust covered all the surfaces, as would be expected from their immersion in the river for several days.

EXERCISE 4.6

Suggest why it was important to find the missing portion of the eye bar.

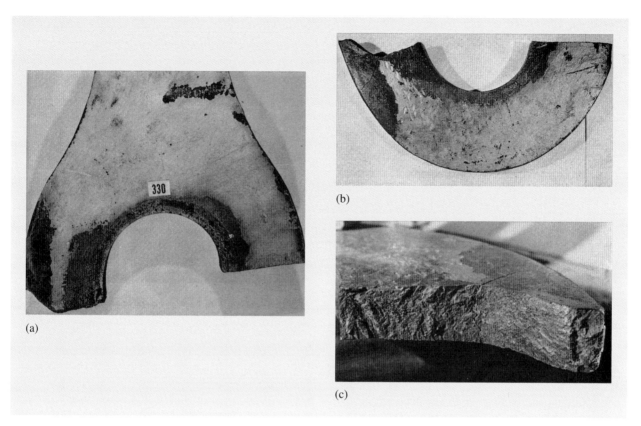

(a)

(b)

(c)

Figure 4.27   The brittle fracture in eye bar 330

When the thin coating of recent red-brown rust was removed gently in the laboratory, the original state of the surface on the lower part of the eye-bar hole, the part showing the brittle fracture, was revealed. Citric acid, present in citrus fruits like lemons, was used to remove the rust. It is a very weak acid, and so its dissolution of red-brown rust is slow. This allowed more control of the cleaning process, minimizing damage to the underlying surface. The overall fracture surface showed very little sign of ductility, except for a small shear lip along a short length of the outer edge of the fracture.

Part of the fracture surface is shown in Figure 4.28. It was noticed that one corner of the inner side of the fracture, i.e. the side next to the pin, showed two curved features of different colour and texture from the rest of the fracture. These zones were very small, measuring only 1.5 mm and 3 mm in diameter respectively; the origin of the larger zone is shown in the figure. They were dark grey, almost black, a tone probably representing Fe_3O_4, the iron oxide formed in low concentrations of oxygen or air: see ☑ **Rusting** ☑. Remnants of the recent red-brown rust were visible in pockets on the rest of the surface. The lines on the curved features pointed back to the inner surface of the eye bar. It was feasible to suggest that the two zones represented brittle cracks present before the final failure that reached a critical size just before the catastrophe.

Figure 4.28 Close-up of the critical defect in the inner edge of the eye bar

origin

☑ Rusting

The reactions of iron and water include several end products, depending on the presence or absence of air, the temperature and the concentrations of salts in solution. The chemical reactions here are for illustration: you don't have to remember them.

The most common product is red-brown rust, formed by the reaction:

$$4Fe + 3O_2 \rightarrow 2Fe_2O_3$$

Note that in the Fe_2O_3 produced, the ratio of iron to oxygen is 1:1.5. The volume of red-brown rust is about 50% greater than that of the metal, and so can enhance crack growth.

Hydration of the oxide is usual in the presence of water:

$$Fe_2O_3 + 2H_2O \rightarrow Fe_2O_3.2H_2O$$

The hydrated oxide is a very weakly protective film because it tends to spall away from the underlying surface in lamellar flakes, exposing a fresh surface to further attack. The volume change associated with producing the hydrated oxide is larger than for the oxide itself owing to the water molecules in the atomic structure.

The reaction of iron with water can also form hydroxides, producing hydrogen gas:

$$Fe + 2H_2O \rightarrow Fe(OH)_2 + H_2$$

$$2Fe + 6H_2O \rightarrow 2Fe(OH)_3 + 3H_2$$

The hydrogen gas may represent a danger if the reactions occur in an enclosed environment, such as a steel tank, for example. Many welders have been injured and killed by explosions when the welding torch penetrates to the interior: the hydrogen is released to mix with air and then explodes.

If the concentration of oxygen is low, then different oxides are formed:

$$2Fe + O_2 \rightarrow 2FeO$$

where the ratio of iron to oxygen is 1:1, and:

$$FeO + Fe_2O_3 \rightarrow Fe_3O_4$$

where the ratio of iron to oxygen is 1:1.3.

Both products are black and form preferentially at high temperatures, such as during forging of hot metal, when they are known as 'black scale'. They are usually removed by treatment with sulphuric acid in large-scale manufacture, a process known as pickling. Black oxide is also formed in central heating systems, since the system is closed to the outer air and oxygen is depleted in the closed water supply by reaction. Hydrogen gas accumulates at the top of the system, and is liberated when the system is bled.

To explore the problem further, the eye bar was examined for signs of further cracks. The mechanism that caused the critical crack was probably at work at other points on the inner surface of the eye bar, so could be tested by several techniques.

Many such sub-critical cracks were found (Figure 4.29), showing that there was a single mechanism at work. The interior of many of the cracks was filled with iron oxides, often present in a lamellar form showing successive and intermittent phases of formation. An adjacent eye bar on the next joint down along the chain was also found to be cracked in a similar way at roughly the same point.

SAQ 4.5 (Learning outcomes 4.7, 4.8 and 4.10)

(a) Describe the construction of eye bar 330 and the position of the critical crack in relation to the stresses on the joint.

(b) Explain why a crack may have formed at that location.

(Hint: bear in mind that a hole in a component represents a stress concentration factor of about three.)

(c) If corrosion is an important failure mechanism, explain why the lower part of the eye is more susceptible than the upper.

The other eye bar of the same joint was located, and showed damage to the hole consistent with having been pulled off the pin. A large burr existed on one side of the hole only, showing that the end had been subjected to a large force in the accident.

2.3.2 Analysis of the eye-bar steel

Many sections were taken of the steel near the fracture to examine its microstructure, and were compared with different parts of the same eye bar as well as with other eye bars. The sections showed a steel core surrounded by a zone that could be identified as being of higher strength due to the presence of martensite.

Martensite is a strong, hard phase of steel usually formed by rapid quenching from a high temperature.

sub-critical cracks

(a)   (b)

Figure 4.29   (a) The inner surface showing sub-critical cracks; (b) micrograph of cracks propagating from the hole surface, 8 mm depth

XPS, X-ray photoelectron spectroscopy, gives information about the elements on the surface of a material. It does this by analysis of the X-ray spectrum emitted by the surface when impinged by the electron beam.

The fracture surface was also analysed by XPS for trace elements that might give a clue to the corrosion processes at work over the 39-year lifetime of the bridge. In addition to small traces of manganese present in the original metal, the researchers found significant traces of sulphur present within the cracks; this is an element not present in the metal itself, indicating an unknown, external source. The sulphur concentration was greatest at the mouth of the crack. The steel had a carbon content of 0.6%, slightly higher than the normal content of mild steel (which is up to about 0.3%).

It was possible that the tiny cracks present on the inner surface of eye bar 330 initiated the collapse by causing brittle fracture. It therefore became important to determine the strength of the steel and, also, its fracture toughness. Steel from eye bar 330 was tested, as well as from other eye bars from the Silver Bridge. Hardness tests across a section though an eye bar showed a soft outer zone, followed by a harder zone and then a softer core (Figure 4.30). The hard zone extended from about 2.5 mm to 9 mm inside the section. This represented the hardened zone produced by quenching the steel during manufacture. The outer layer of the bar showed loss of carbon due to the heat treatment during manufacture.

Charpy impact tests at several laboratories showed the toughness to fall with lowering temperature, with a low value at or near the freezing point of 0 °C (Figure 4.31), a temperature close to that experienced at the bridge at the time of the accident.

Small samples cut from eye-bar material were also tested in simple tension at 25 °C, and gave the following results:

yield strength of outer layers = 590 MPa
tensile strength of outer layers = 835 MPa

yield strength of inner layers = 490 MPa
tensile strength of inner layers = 810 MPa.

All the samples showed high ductility with a reduction in cross-sectional area of nearly 50%.

Figure 4.30 Hardness variation across the eye bar

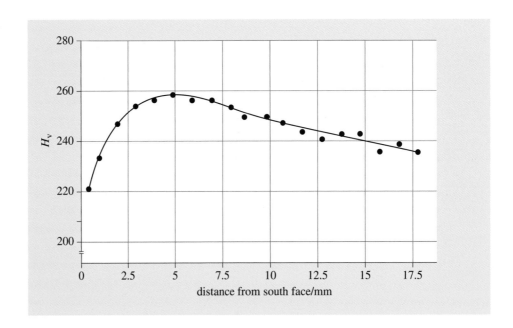

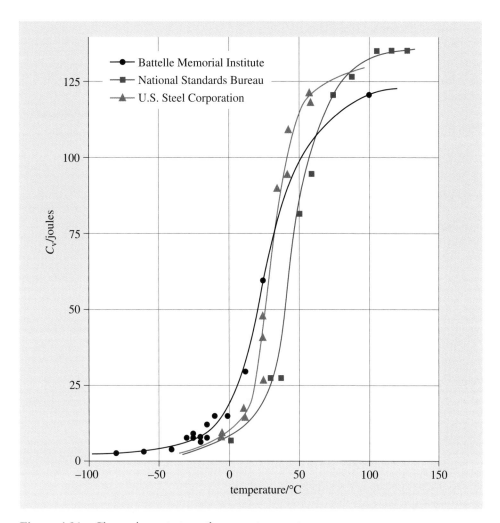

Figure 4.31   Charpy impact strength versus temperature

2.3.3 Simulated environmental tests

The investigators wanted to know about the fatigue properties of the component, to find a feasible explanation of why it took 39 years for the eye bar to break. They needed information on the several stress corrosion mechanisms that were possible in the material, including hydrogen embrittlement, the effects of sulphur compounds such as H_2S (hydrogen sulphide) and the effects of moisture and salt. Notched eye-bar material was loaded to failure in various environments.

In fact, no evidence emerged for hydrogen embrittlement, and a wet environment in the laboratory tests had no effect on the rate of crack propagation. However, the life of the steel samples was reduced substantially by hydrogen sulphide, a conclusion that appeared to correlate well with the detection of sulphur in the critical crack (and other, sub-critical cracks).

2.3.4 Stress concentration at joint

Although it is known that a round hole in a flat sample will theoretically produce a stress concentration of about 3, the issue was decided experimentally. A tensile test at 25 °C was undertaken on an intact eye-bar–pin assembly from the bridge, being some 8 m long and from a lower part of the chain. It yielded at about 7 MN, and fractured in the shank at a stress of about 770 MPa. The yield stress in the shank was about 520 MPa, and the failed eye bar showed ductile behaviour with a reduction in area of 30% at an elongation of 8.5 %. By putting strain gauges at various points in the hole of the bar, the stress concentration was calculated to be about 2.62 at the opposing faces of the inner side of the hole where fracture had occurred in eye bar 330.

EXERCISE 4.7

Suggest why, in the tensile tests, fracture occurred in the shank rather than at the hole of the eye bar. What factors contribute to where failure occurs?

It is worth emphasizing that stress concentrations are of less importance in ductile compared with brittle-type failures. After all, a material that usually fails in a ductile manner, such as steel, can yield locally at the root of a notch or the edge of a hole. By contrast, during brittle fracture there is no mechanism for absorbing excessive load by deforming plastically, and the stress at the root of a crack may be extremely high.

The experiment established that brittle cracks had not developed in the lower eye bar: if they had, this test bar would have failed at the hole rather than in the shank.

2.3.5 Fretting fatigue

An additional possibility was considered. It was known that there was significant movement of the bridge during passage of traffic, because users had noticed it many times when crossing. The joints would thus have been subjected to rotary motion around the pin in order to accommodate such vibrations. Could these have caused fatigue crack growth at the bearing surfaces?

Contact between a circular and a flat plate creates so-called Hertzian stresses at the contact zone: compressive at the centre, and surrounded by a tensile zone. A similar effect will occur at a circular pin joint, provided there is some clearance between the two parts. In addition, there could be considerable wear caused by corrosion. Rusting would create particles of $Fe_2O_3.2H_2O$, which, being harder than the steel, would act as an abrasive powder as the surfaces moved against one another. The fact that the rust particles had a larger volume than the metal they replaced would also stimulate wear. The inner surfaces of the eye-bar holes showed deep grooves (Figure 4.29a), indicating fretting action. Could fretting have initiated critical cracks?

To test this hypothesis, pin and collar shapes were machined from eye bar 330 (away from the region of the actual failure), fitted together and then rotated so that the pin acted against the collar. The results are shown in Figure 4.32. Even with the effects of fretting, the material around the eye still showed a higher fatigue life than the material in the shank.

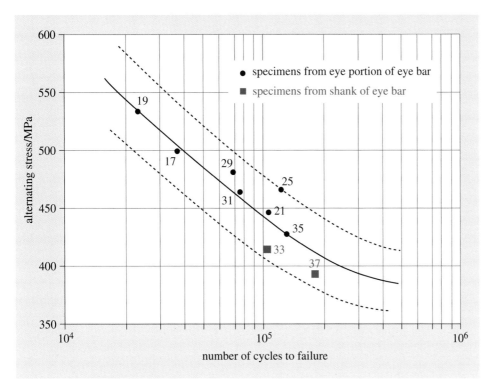

Figure 4.32   Fretting fatigue

SAQ 4.6 (Learning outcome 4.12)

Suggest how fretting fatigue could occur at a pin joint in the main chains of the Silver Bridge. Indicate the most likely place for such a problem, and compare the actual position of the critical and sub-critical cracks on eye bar 330, drawing any appropriate conclusions.

There is no doubt that fretting action on the inner surface of eye-bar joint 330 occurred during its 39-year life. The surface next to the critical crack is very rough indeed, showing deep corrugations aligned circumferentially: that is, at right angles to the sub-critical cracks seen in Figure 4.29(a). There appears to be no obvious correlation between the crack positions and the corrugations, however. Fretting action will have been most severe on the highest joints of the chain where the load on the joint was greatest.

2.3.6 Residual stress

One factor that can cause serious problems in any material is the presence of residual tensile stress. The problem often arises as a direct result of manufacturing, when hot material is shaped and then allowed to cool to ambient temperatures. For large castings like those needed to make the eye bars, such residual stress would be modified by the subsequent heat treatment to strengthen the steel, but had to be studied as part of the research effort into the catastrophic failure of the bridge.

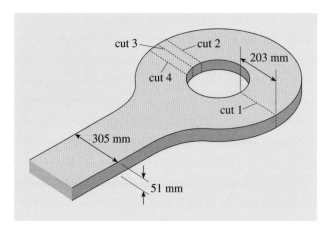

Figure 4.33   Cuts made for residual-stress measurements

The residual stress was investigated using several methods, including the destructive technique of removing metal layer by layer, as well as by drilling holes in the suspect sample. The surface strain was monitored by strain gauges, which indicated that there was significant stress in the eye bars near the critical inner surface next to the pin. The cuts made in order to measure the residual stress are shown in Figure 4.33.

The researchers reported that close to the edge of the hole in each eye bar, residual stresses were extremely high as a proportion of the total yield stress. They plotted the hoop tensile stress against the distance from the edge of the hole to produce a graph as shown in Figure 4.34. The upper curves show the residual stress in the inner surface of the eye bar to be of the greatest magnitude.

Such large stresses as those shown in Figure 4.34 point to the reason why the crack grew initially, and then, when it had reached a critical depth of about 3 mm, catastrophically. On the inner surface the largest stresses observed fall above the top measure of the graph at 160 MPa, the greatest being 190 MPa, nearly a third of the yield strength of the material. The stress tends to drop inside the bar, although in different ways; at cut 4, a compressive state is reached in the middle of the bar.

Although not sufficiently recognized at the time, residual stress in the inner edge of the eye of the bars was clearly a significant factor in the disaster. Whether or not other eye bars were examined in a similar way remains at present unknown, and the follow-up with the makers, US Steel, also unclear. The residual tensile stresses will have been formed during casting and the subsequent heat treatment, and exposed at the inner edge when the central holes were machined out. Records of the heat treatment eye bar by eye bar should have been inspected by the investigators, but whether they did see such records remains unknown. Whether US Steel knew about the problem at all also remains unknown.

2.4 Design of the bridge

The design of the original structure was governed by applicable standards in 1926. The official inquiry found that the design and build fell within those limits, the most important being the allowable stress in the eye-bar chain of 345 MPa. The steel was to be made with a maximum elastic limit of 520 MPa, with a safety

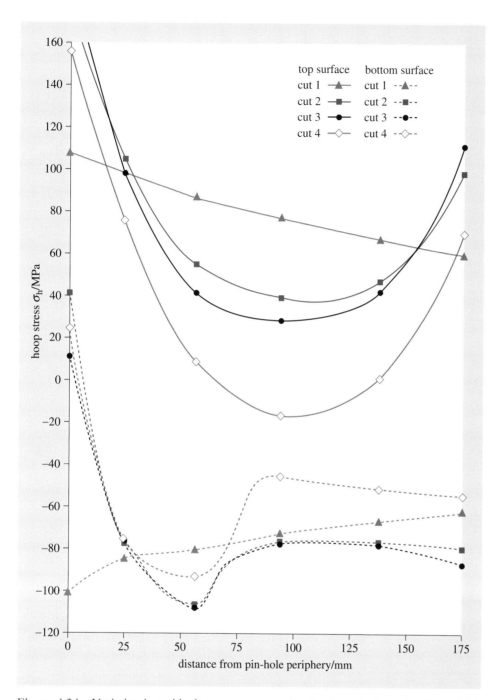

Figure 4.34   Variation in residual stress across eye bar for the cuts shown in Figure 4.33

factor on the strength of the steel of 2.75. It was argued at the time that over 70% of the load was from the self-weight of the structure. Other suspension bridges of the same time were built with higher safety factors, however. A similar design of eye-bar chain in a larger bridge at Florianopolis in Brazil was given a safety factor of 4.61 using an allowable stress of 320 MPa. The bridge used four eye bars rather than two, so had greater redundancy. ☑ **Safety factors** ☑ of 4.6 to 4.7 based on yield stress were usual in wire suspension bridges (such as the Golden Gate bridge in San Francisco).

☑ Safety factors

The safety factor chosen for any structure is simply an expression of the state of knowledge (or lack thereof) at the time, and should allow for any future uncertainties as well as present uncertainties, such as quality of the parts used in the structure. So the safety factor might be termed an uncertainty factor. When knowledge of strength and quality is poor, then the safety factor is high. Thus at the time of building railway bridges in Britain in the 1850s, cast iron was widely used as a principal structural material. Steel was not available until much later. It was known that cast iron was brittle in tension, and following early tragedies, it was specified that a safety factor of 6 should be used for railway bridge design. This safety factor allowed for stress concentrations such as blow holes and sharp corners in beams, although it could be exceeded if such defects were close to one another, when the effect of one is multiplied by the effect of the other. Thus a spherical blow hole ($K_t \approx 2$) next to a circular hole ($K_t \approx 3$) gives a net effect of $K_t \approx 6$.

The safety factor is most critical and important for the most highly loaded parts of a structure, simply because they will be closest to failure if, for whatever reason, the maximum permissible load is somehow exceeded. Nowadays, structures are designed for maximum loading from a variety of sources that are often difficult to predict with high confidence. Those factors include:

wind loading

earthquake loading

precipitation such as snow and rain.

Some are created by the weather, a notoriously difficult area to predict, and others by movements in the earth's crust (also difficult to predict). However, hurricanes and earthquakes do tend to occur in well-defined areas of the world, and so structures built in those zones will have a higher safety factor than elsewhere to allow for the extra risk there. All these natural phenomena will produce extra loads on a structure, and frequently cause catastrophic failure. Thus a double-deck highway collapsed on itself during the San Francisco earthquake of 1989 (killing 23 drivers on the lower deck at the time). Several stadiums in Europe collapsed with heavy casualties during the winter of 2005/6 owing to high snow loading.

However, little was apparently known then about the problem of stress corrosion cracking, although the type of strengthened steel used in the eye bars had been tested before use for its fatigue properties. It was known that the material would be subject to rusting, but it was thought that painting would prevent the problem becoming serious. Unfortunately the design of the pin joints left them completely exposed to the weather, and water could gather at the lowest points within the joint. Such hidden parts of the joint could not be painted owing to their inaccessibility, so were left unprotected. Moreover, the eye-bar joint could not be inspected without disassembly, an impractical solution for a suspension bridge.

SAQ 4.7 (Learning outcome 4.13)

(a) Describe the known problems of stress corrosion cracking that had occurred historically at the time of the design of the Silver Bridge, and their known solutions.

(b) What other problems, apart from stress corrosion, could have been foreseen at the critical eye-bar joints? Suggest measures that could have been taken to prevent the problem.

Cable suspension bridges are also corrosion-sensitive, the most recent example being the corrosion at the base of the main hangers of the first Severn suspension bridge. Although the high-tensile steel wires had been galvanized, salt water collected in the joints at the road decks and penetrated to the interior of the joints, causing breakage of the seal. The zinc coating corrodes preferentially, but once this is consumed then rusting of the core will occur. All had to be replaced at high cost during the 1990s.

2.5 Failure sequence

Following the discovery of the broken eye bar near the top of the northern suspension chain on the Ohio side of the bridge (Figure 4.25), it was possible to reconstruct the sequence of events during the collapse.

When the side chain separated, the entire structure was destabilized, simply because all the loads it supported were immediately transferred to the adjacent parts of the bridge. With its support along the north side of the bridge destroyed, the road deck below the broken chain started tipping over to the north. The hangers holding it up on the south side started breaking, and the deck below the tower broke away. The road deck crashed to the ground on the Ohio bank of the river, taking its vehicles with it as it fell.

The Ohio tower was affected rapidly by the break in eye bar 330, and it leaned over to the north east, with buckling and fractures of its bracing elements below the top. The main road deck in the centre of the bridge was also tipping and dropping as the tower toppled over. As the tower fell, it pulled the south main chain over with it, putting it under enormous lateral load. In the main span, fractures of the hangers occurred on the south side of the deck; as the main chain fell to the north, it impacted the north tower, and eye-bar joints started breaking in the south chain. It was followed by main-chain joint fractures near the West Virginia tower. According to the official account of the disaster, these events occurred up to about 10 seconds after the fracture of eye bar 330. During this phase the road deck broke in the middle, taking its vehicles down into the river. The visual sequence is summarized by one of the eyewitnesses who was about a quarter of a mile away downstream on the West Virginia river bank:

> I turned around and looked and saw the Ohio towers (*sic*) falling. The tower legs seemed to twist counterclockwise (when viewed from the top) and fall upstream and towards the center of the river. The center span of the bridge broke in the middle and fell straight down. It looked as though the cars on the center span all fell with the bridge and looked like they were falling in a funnel – some falling backward, some falling forward. After the center span fell, the West Virginia towers (*sic*) and span fell … the bridge was all down in a matter of five seconds as I estimate it …

The West Virginia tower was one of the last main parts of the bridge to fall, dropping into the river and facing towards the east. At the end of about a minute the entire superstructure, apart from the stone piers, had disappeared (Figure 4.24).

DVD

An animation of the collapse of the bridge can be seen as part of the programme 'The Silver Bridge disaster and its legacy' on the course DVD.

2.6 Aftermath

In the immediate aftermath of the disaster, it was vital to prevent any further collapses, especially on bridges of similar design. Two other bridges were built to a design similar to that of the Silver Bridge, one upstream at St Mary's, West Virginia and the other in Brazil at Florianopolis. The bridge upstream on the Ohio river, at St Mary's, was the focus of concern, and it was closed to traffic immediately after the disaster. The eye-bar design was actually quite widespread in other bridges, but frequently eye bars were provided not in pairs but in multiple connections, increasing the safety factor significantly. In the case of a single eye-bar failure, the others could support the load until repairs were made. This is certainly true of many British chain suspension bridges as well as US structures.

The inquiry recommended several key measures, which were enacted by President Johnson. They included:

1   identification of safety-critical parts of existing bridges, and the materials of construction

2   examination of possible failure mechanisms, including corrosion fatigue and stress corrosion fatigue

3   development of new ways of inspecting critical parts of such bridges

4   development of safeguards against future problems, including modified standards

5   expansion of the knowledge of corrosion problems.

A nationwide inspection of existing bridges (about 1 million) was quickly undertaken, and many problems identified and corrected.

SAQ 4.8 (Learning outcomes 4.11 and 4.13)

Describe the failure sequence of the Silver Bridge in December 1967, indicating the direct cause of the accident and any contributing factors that led to the failure. Include in your answer the evidence for the particular causes you mention.

In terms of current knowledge of failure analysis, there are several gaps that could have been addressed at the time. In particular, the fact that the critical crack occurred in an eye bar *below* the top of one of the towers suggests very strongly that the level of residual stress varied between the eye bars. The origin of the eye bar analysed and discussed above is not stated in the official report, and it also appears that only this one eye bar was actually studied for residual stress. It would have been of great interest to have seen the variation of residual stress levels across the upper eye bars, because it is the only explanation of the formation of a critical crack in an eye bar exposed to lower imposed dead and live loads.

A second question arises about the source of the sulphur found in the critical crack initiation region. The official report points towards H_2S, but this is a rare gas to have occurred in an open environment. Sulphur dioxide is a much more common pollutant, and could have been produced by a local power station using high-sulphur West Virginia coal. There was also a foundry in Point Pleasant, close to the east side of the bridge, which probably produced quantities of the gas during smelting.

A subsequent court case was brought by the injured victims and relatives of the deceased, alleging negligence on the part of the builders of the bridge. The case was rejected on the grounds that stress corrosion cracking of the kind found in the critical eye bar was not known at the time the bridge was designed. Although the plaintiffs received no compensation, the disaster had at least raised the importance of thorough inspection of an ageing infrastructure. However, bridge failures unfortunately continue to occur.

3 CASE STUDY 2: MIANUS RIVER DISASTER

After the inspection of bridges across the USA initiated by the Silver Bridge accident, many bridges were repaired (if defects were found). It might then be expected that further disasters would be eliminated entirely. Not so.

It came as a shock to the country when another disaster occurred in 1983, at the crossing of Interstate highway 95 over the Mianus River in Connecticut. The bridge had been built in 1958, and so was about 25 years old when tragedy struck. The accident happened at 1.30 a.m. on 28 June 1983, when a steel-framed concrete slab forming the deck of three lanes of the eastbound highway suddenly fell into the river below. Traffic was light, but two heavy trucks and two cars plunged 20 m into the void (Figure 4.35). The drivers of several other cars saw what had happened and luckily were able to stop. The weather was mild on the morning of the accident, with little wind and no rain. The temperature was 21 °C.

3.1 Bridge structure

The road was supported by more than 20 reinforced concrete piers embedded into either the river approaches or the river bed itself (Figure 4.36). The bridge was 2656 feet (810 m) long and 70 feet (21 m) above the river at its highest point at the centre. As the pictures show, it was a skew bridge, i.e. with the deck sections built at an angle so that the concrete piers in the river were aligned parallel to the main direction of flow of the river. It supported six lanes of highway with an expansion joint running down the middle, and so effectively was two parallel bridges that functioned independently of one another.

Figure 4.35   Mianus River road bridge disaster

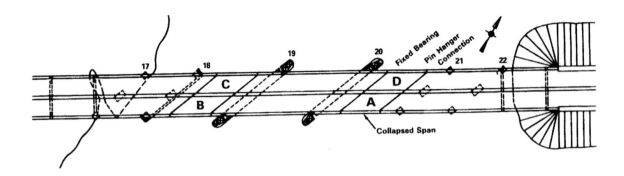

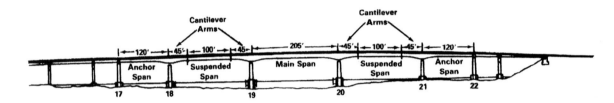

Figure 4.36   Structure of the Mianus River bridge

The road-deck structure consisted of so-called anchor spans at each bank, followed by a suspended deck and a single main span. There were thus four suspended decks in the structure (A, B, C and D in Figure 4.36). Each individual suspended deck was 12.5 m wide and 30.5 m long, corresponding to the width of one side of the roadway and the length between the cantilever arms respectively (Figure 4.36; here dimensions are shown in the original Imperial units of the report). Each deck weighed about 996 kN, and consisted of a steel frame supporting a concrete roadway. The reason for such a form of construction was to enable the decks to expand and contract with changes in ambient temperature. The expansion joints comprised two so-called pillow block assemblies on the inner side of the deck (the long side closest to the spine of the bridge), and two hanger assemblies on the outer side (the long side furthest from the spine). The pillow blocks were effectively flexible hinges taking up any expansion on the shorter side of the deck, while the hangers took up expansion on the longer side of the deck.

SAQ 4.9 (Learning outcomes 4.7 and 4.14)

(a) Given that the coefficient of linear expansion of steel is about $11 \times 10^{-6} \, \text{K}^{-1}$, calculate the change in length of a steel beam 30.5 m long for a temperature change of −50 to +50 °C.

The change in length from an original length L_0 for a temperature change of ΔT is given by the formula:

$$\Delta L = \alpha L_0 \Delta T$$

where α is the coefficient of linear expansion.

(b) What minimum clearance should be given at the joint between adjacent decks along the length of the roadway? What minimum clearance should be given between adjacent decks across the width of the road?

(c) Supposing that there were no expansion joints, what stress would be generated in the bridge? The elastic modulus of steel is 210 GPa.

(Hint: you need to calculate the strain associated with the change in length.)

Further devices, such as rocker bearings at piers 18, 19 and 20, were also designed to help relieve thermal expansion and contraction loads. Piers 17, 21 and 22 had fixed bearings (Figure 4.36).

3.2 Sequence of events

3.2.1 Warning signs

Interesting statements were given after the event by two truck drivers who had passed over that section of the bridge just before the accident. The first driver was driving over the bridge at 12.45 a.m. on 28 June in an articulated lorry in the slow or outside lane. He saw, and then struck, a large crack in the carriageway, which almost caused him to lose control of his truck. He estimated the crack to be 150 to 200 mm wide and 100 mm deep, running diagonally across the road. The second truck driver said he was travelling east on the same road at 1.10 a.m. when he hit what he thought was a large pothole, with such force that it caused his vehicle to swerve into the left lane and almost hit the inside guard rail. They both said that the condition of the road was generally very poor (with many potholes), but they had never experienced anything as bad as this before.

Deep potholes are a hazard all drivers on concrete roads must face, especially in the spring and summer after a hard winter, when ☑ **freeze–thaw cycles** ☑ occur by water pooling in cracks in the road, causing spalling and loss of concrete. The erosion cycle starts with small cracks in the concrete, which grow almost imperceptibly until they become a deep pothole. Such serious potholes can cause not just damage to the suspension of a car, but also accidents if the car spins out of control.

☑ Freeze–thaw cycles

One of the ways water acts as a mechanism of deterioration is by freeze–thaw cycling, when it repeatedly freezes and melts. Because the volume of a given mass of ice is greater than the same mass of water, rock crevices that fill with water can be split apart by the water as it freezes to ice. The density of ice at 0 °C is 920 kg m^{-3}, compared with 1000 kg m^{-3} for water at the same temperature. So, when the water freezes, it expands by 8%; this exerts considerable pressure on the walls of the crevice, causing the crevice to expand. If the crevice is a crack, then the natural consequence is that the crack grows in length (Figure 4.37). Freeze–thaw cycling is a common physical mode of ▷

weathering, and is often the cause of rock falls in mountains. Householders experience the problem for themselves when a water pipe bursts in the thaw after a heavy frost. Although the damage may be done when the ice first forms, it is only when it melts that the damage is made apparent by the flood created.

The expansion of about 8% by volume that water undergoes when it freezes has few, if any, parallels with other fusion processes of common compounds, although many corrosion reactions involve expansion since the compounds formed often have a lower density than the starting material. Thus rusting, when iron is converted to its oxide, involves a volume expansion of no less than 50%, which helps explain why rusting in enclosed environments can create serious structural problems. Rusting of steel reinforcement bars in concrete can exert pressures so great as to crack the matrix, causing lumps of concrete to fall from motorway bridges, for example.

Figure 4.37 Freeze–thaw cracking of boulder

Both drivers thought that their incidents had occurred in the vicinity of the later accident, but they had not reported these incidents to the police or highway authority. However, as the incidents took place only 45 and 20 minutes before the disaster respectively, it is unlikely that the traffic could have been halted in time even if they had been reported.

But the two independent incidents do suggest that the deck had dropped from the south-east hanger by then, to leave the 100 mm drop in the upper road surface; this presumably was at its greatest in the slow lane, near to the failed south-east hanger.

3.2.2 Accident witnesses

There were several eyewitness accounts that showed how the final fall occurred. In the words of the official report:

> At 1.30 a.m. … eastbound traffic on Interstate Route 95 (I-95) was light as it approached the highway bridge … An automobile was in the median lane of the three-lane eastbound roadway, a tractor-semitrailer was abreast in the center lane, and another tractor-semitrailer was in the curb lane and slightly ahead of the other two vehicles. According to the driver and passenger in a car following these three vehicles moving at highway speeds, there was a sudden flash of light and the highway overhead lighting on the bridge went

out. The driver of the following car said that at the same time the brake lights of the two trucks came on, and the semitrailer of the truck in the curb lane began to change its alignment with the tractor as though it was starting to jackknife. Fearing an accident, the driver of the following car braked his vehicle hard, and suddenly the three vehicles ahead disappeared from view. The driver stopped the car in the center lane of the bridge. When he got out, he saw that the car was about 6 feet from the edge of a void where a section of the bridge had fallen into the river 70 feet below.

The driver of the following car had been extremely lucky. But then an unfortunate incident occurred:

> Because the driver and passenger were concerned about their car being struck from the rear, they moved away from the car quickly. The driver … left the car lights on but did not switch on the hazard warning signals. The driver saw an eastbound automobile approaching and tried to flag it to a stop by waving his arms. … It plunged into the void and landed upside down in the river below.

Fortunately other traffic did stop when he activated the hazard warning lights. There were other witnesses on boats moored at a marina in the river 600 feet south of the bridge. The report continues:

> One witness, who was lying on his back on the deck of a boat and looking up at the bridge, saw a lightpole and then a section of the … bridge begin to shake and then fall into the river. Several witnesses saw the first tractor-semitrailer and the first automobile fall with the bridge … The witnesses all agreed that the east end of the span fell first.

The rescue parties found three dead and three very severely injured in their vehicles.

The total weight of the two trucks was about 676 kN, so with the two cars this would have given a total weight (or live load) on the span of nearly 725 kN at the time of the accident. The police estimated that the trucks were travelling at 41 to 59 mph.

3.3 The investigation

The NTSB produced its report of the accident in 11 months, a much shorter time than for the Silver Bridge inquiry. There had been no total loss of the structure, but rather a limited catastrophic failure (Figure 4.38), so the evidence was directly accessible and the critical components that had failed could be examined much more easily. The deck that had fallen (deck A in Figure 4.36) lay slightly to one side of its original position. One side of the deck was seriously damaged, and there was much corrosion visible on the bearings that held it to the superstructure. The hangers, at what the report calls the south-east and north-east corners of the deck, were most seriously affected. These were subjected to closer scrutiny to determine what parts had failed and how that failure had come about. A reasonably clear picture of the sequence of events began to emerge, and when the causes were established some awkward issues would arise.

3.3.1 Hanger bearing structure

The hanger bearing of immediate attention was that at the south-east corner of the deck slab. It showed substantial corrosion as well as fractures, and to a much

failed hanger

Figure 4.38   Failure of suspended span, looking north-east

greater extent than the north-east hanger bearing: see ☑ **Corrosion of reinforced concrete structures** ☑. Each hanger joint consisted of two vertical bars with holes at either end, by which they were held onto pins through the two girders. The joint is shown schematically in Figure 4.39(a) and the detail of the pin in Figure 4.39(b). The clearance between the cantilever and the suspended girders was greater than the allowance calculated above, and was 102 mm. Each bar was 2 m long (or 1.4 m from centre to centre of the holes), was 406 mm wide and consisted of 38 mm thick steel.

The pin part of the joint consisted nominally of a cylindrical steel bearing 178 mm long and the same in diameter. However, the diameter had been changed slightly, presumably to accommodate a smaller hole in the hangers, and it is not shown on the sections of Figure 4.39. The diameter had been reduced by 6 mm by machining, so leaving sharp corners in the cylinders next to the hangers. The ends of the cylinders were also chamfered.

The cylindrical bearing was held in place with the hangers by a 25 mm diameter, 362 mm long bolt threaded at each end to accept hexagonal nuts. Washers were fitted on the bolt at several points. The first was welded to the web of the girder, then a 6.35 mm thick spacer washer was fitted in the 9.5 mm space with the hanger. On the outside of the hanger was fitted another spacer washer (8 mm thick) under an outermost cap of the same thickness, to which the hexagonal nut was attached at the threaded end of the transverse bolt running though the whole bearing.

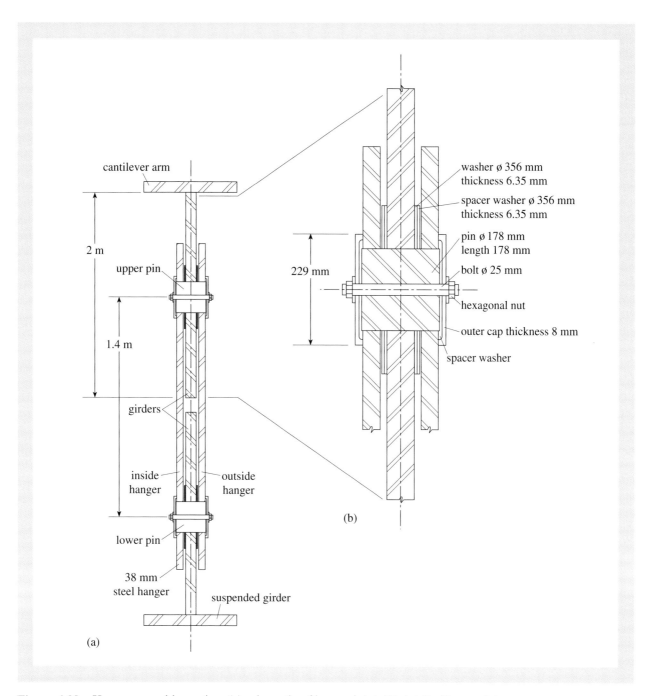

Figure 4.39 Hanger assembly section: (a) schematic of hanger joint; (b) detail of hanger joint

▽ Corrosion of reinforced concrete structures

Serious damage can occur to reinforced concrete structures (especially bridges) through rusting of the steel reinforcement bars buried within the structures. Rusting of the hangers of the Mianus River bridge was enhanced by salting of the roads during the harsh winters experienced in New England, as well as by being in a marine environment. Uncoated steel bars buried in concrete normally have a degree of protection through an oxide film formed on their surface by reaction with the hydroxyl ions present in the curing cement. Although the reactions in curing cement are complex, there are some useful general points. As the cement hardens with time, polymeric silicate is produced, together with heat since the reaction is exothermic. The pH of the water in the pores of the cement also rises in parallel with polymerisation, peaking at a value of about 12.6.

The pH of a substance indicates how acidic or alkaline it is. A substance with a pH of 7 is neutral; pH values lower than 7 indicate acidity, while pH values higher than 7 indicate alkalinity. A pH of 12.6 is highly alkaline.

Problems arise because of percolation of rainwater and run-off through the concrete structure. Slightly acidic rain (containing carbon dioxide and nitric acid) can, over time, neutralise the alkalinity in the pores and attack the passive layer on the reinforcement bars. The initial result may be streaks of red-brown rust from the dissolved layer forming on external surfaces. The attack is enhanced by chloride ions present from deliberate salting in winter and sea salt carried in the rain. The next phase of attack involves expansion of the rust layer by up to 50% in volume, putting the surrounding concrete under severe stress. Brittle cracks form at the interface, and will grow with continued rusting (Figure 4.40).

Crack growth will also be enhanced by freeze–thaw action in northern climates, especially for horizontal cracks in exposed locations on a structure. Water expands by 8% when it freezes, and when repeated this exerts high loads within cracks. Exposed structures like bridges are especially vulnerable.

External spalling often follows as the cracks meet the outer surfaces, the course of events being determined by many factors, including the local environment, the geometry of the structure and so on. The integrity of the structure will be affected if the cracking occurs at, or near, zones of high load, such as joints and the centres of beams. The costs of replacement will often be very high, since once attack becomes visible the structure is beyond repair.

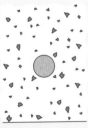  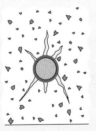 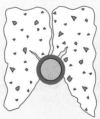

before corrosion   build-up of corrosion products   further corrosion surface cracks stains   eventual spallation corroded bar exposed

Figure 4.40 The corrosion cycle of uncoated steel

3.3.2 Extent of corrosion

The south-east bearing showed the most severe corrosion, primarily rusting within the spaces of the pin assembly. After the accident, some parts were found still attached to the web of the cantilever girder on the standing bridge: the upper pin, the inner hanger and most of the pin bolt. However, the bolt had fractured at the upper and outer corner, and completely separated. The fracture surface showed all the signs of fatigue: a 19 mm deep curvilinear area extending from the top of the pin, noticeably discoloured and quite different from the rest of the fracture.

There was extensive corrosion of the parts of the upper pin, mainly between the welded washers (W in Figure 4.41) and spacer washers (SW). The corrosion products, mainly $Fe_2O_3.2H_2O$, were packed tightly into the gap between the two parts, as shown by the section of Figure 4.41. The rust had several effects: the inner hanger was itself pushed out from the web of the girder, and the outer spacer washer was permanently dished outwards – as can be seen especially at lower left in Figure 4.41. A close-up of the distorted zone is shown in Figure 4.42. There is a deep crevice in the upper (welded) washer at the edge of the web of the girder. Corrosion has pushed the spacer washer out about 20 mm.

The inner hanger showed severe corrosion on the lower bearing surface of the hole. Although many parts of the hanger assembly had fallen into the river below, they were recovered and the lower pin was found to be tapered from the extent of the rusting. Similar distortion of the spacer washer had occurred, to the extent of about 25 mm outwards. The bottom inner side of the cylindrical pin had fractured and separated, just like the upper pin. Extensive rusting masked the fracture surface. There were extensive traces of rust marks on the girders adjacent to both hanger assemblies, some of which can be seen at the north-east corner shown in Figure 4.38, right next to the hanger bar still dangling from its pin.

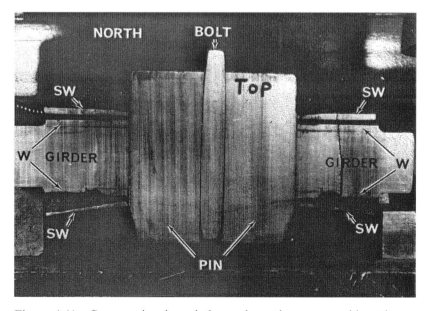

Figure 4.41   Cross section through the south-east hanger assembly at the upper pin, showing corrosion

Figure 4.42 Detail of corrosion from Figure 4.41

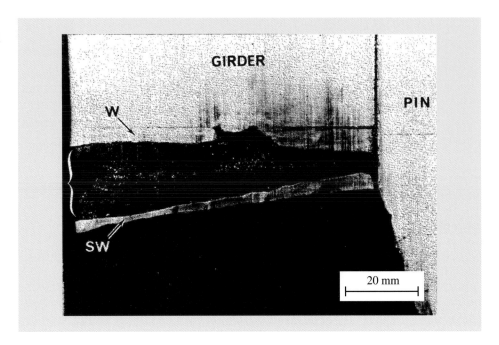

The visible deterioration of both washer surfaces to account for this loss of steel, by crevice corrosion, pitting and uniform removal from the two inner surfaces, is evident from Figures 4.41 and 4.42.

3.3.3 Failed bolts

Two of the three pin bolts that fell from the bridge were found. One was presumed to have come from the lower part of the south-east joint, the other from the north-east joint. They had both fractured at the threaded end, where the thread grooves represented a large stress concentration. They appeared to have failed owing to ductile overload, although diagnosis proved difficult given the corrosion present on both parts. Further rusting after a fracture can of course obliterate the original evidence, especially if the fracture occurred early in the failure sequence.

3.3.4 Other suspended decks

Also of some interest for comparative analysis was the state of the other three suspended decks, B, C and D of Figure 4.36. Dishing and distortion of the outer pin caps was prevalent, tending to be greater on the outer rather than the inner sides of the joints. In one case, a very badly distorted pin bolt was burnt off and the nut removed after the load had been supported by other means. The official report records:

> When the pin cap was removed, black rust flowed out of the connection. The Chief of the Review and Analysis Branch, Bridge Division of the FHWA [Federal Highways Works Authority] who witnessed the pin cap removal testified at the public hearing: '... there is no way that I would have ever believed or conceived that the amount of deterioration behind that pin cap would have been there. I never in my wildest days have seen that amount of deterioration, and I don't think short of taking that pin cap off, anyone else could judge that that would be the case.'

It was becoming abundantly clear that all the hanger joints had rusted severely, and questions about the maintenance and inspection activities carried out on the bridge would be raised.

3.3.5 Bridge loading

The design codes for this type of bridge when it was designed in 1955, and then built in 1958, specified that all parts be capable of resisting dead load, live load, impact loads, wind loads and any other external forces. The dead load was essentially the weight of the deck, 996 kN, and a live load was assumed to comprise three tractor truck/semi-trailers in each of the three lanes (a rather low total of 409 kN – the total live load on the deck at the time of the accident, from just two articulated lorries, was actually nearly 700 kN). An impact load was assumed at nearly 90 kN, thus giving a total of nearly 1500 kN spread over the four deck bearings. Assuming equal division of the total load, each bearing would have to support a maximum load of about 370 kN.

It is interesting to note that the live load for such a structure forms a much higher proportion of the total load than that on the individual joints at the Silver Bridge. This simply reflects the very different way the loads are distributed in the two structures. It also accounts for the much greater importance of fatigue as a possible failure mode at the bearings of the Mianus River bridge compared with Silver Bridge. Fatigue is more likely when there are greater fluctuations in load.

3.3.6 Corrosion forces

It was of some interest to the NTSB inquiry to estimate the forces exerted by rusting in the joints. Essentially, the force of rusting is caused by the much larger volume of hydrated iron oxide compared with the original steel. If rust is formed in an enclosed space, it will act against the weaker constraint – the spacer washer in this case – forcing it outwards and distorting it (Figures 4.41 and 4.42). With the density of hydrated red rust being about 3 g cm^{-3}, compared with a steel density of 7.8 g cm^{-3}, there is a volume increase of over 100% as a direct result of the corrosion.

A consultant briefed by the NTSB estimated that a little less than 12 MPa pressure would be needed to overcome the frictional force between the parts and push the joint apart. He assumed a friction coefficient of 0.75 between the steel bolt and washers, together with a maximum load on the bearing of 120 MPa. Other estimates suggested that rusting could produce pressures as high as 30–50 MPa, well above the critical level estimated by the consultant. The effect of any free water in the cavity could add another 5 MPa to the internal pressure by freeze–thaw pressure.

SAQ 4.10 (Learning outcomes 4.2, 4.3 and 4.7)

(a) Estimate the range of loads that would have been exerted by rusting on the spacer washer fitted over the pin behind the hanger, on either the top or the lower pin.

(b) Assuming that the rust consisted of hydrated Fe_2O_3, explain how the process may have occurred.

(c) Knowing that black iron oxide (Fe_3O_4) has a density of 5.18 g cm^{-3}, indicate how the pressure exerted by this oxide would compare with the brown hydrated oxide.

3.4 Failure sequence

Following their inspection, the NTSB investigators were able to indicate the failure sequence for the fallen deck. The hanger joint at the south-east corner showed multistage failure. This proceeded as follows.

1   The initiating event was the destruction of the lower pin by rusting, and may have occurred many weeks or even years before the final accident (Figure 4.43 Box A).

2   The inner hanger had been pushed off the lower pin by corrosion between the washers so that the load on the upper pin was effectively doubled (Figure 4.43 Box A).

3   The upper part of the outer hanger had already been moved by corrosion between the washers along its pin, and the double load was concentrated at the sharp corner machined into the pin. It was here that a fatigue crack initiated and grew slowly, with time, to criticality (Figure 4.43 Box B).

The growth phase was essentially still unknown because the timing of the failure of the lower pin was so uncertain. The highway was very well used, since it is a major artery between New York and the industrial states of Connecticut and Massachusetts. Presumably most of the fatigue growth would have been caused by heavy trucks moving in the slow lane, that is, directly over the bearing at the edge of the bridge. However, the NTSB did not attempt to correlate bridge usage with fatigue crack growth.

As soon as the fatigue crack reached a critical size, it will have grown catastrophically and fractured through, leaving the road deck balanced precariously on just three remaining bearings. From the witness evidence of the previous drivers, this event is likely to have occurred shortly before the final accident. The deep cavity in the highway reported by a truck driver three-quarters of an hour before the accident was probably the first indication that the fatigue crack had grown to a critical size, allowing the deck to drop about 100 mm. If there had been a greater time interval between this drop and the final collapse of the suspended span, many other drivers would have been alerted and perhaps given a warning to the police, thus preventing the eventual fatalities.

The final event in the sequence occurred when three vehicles drove over the unstable slab deck simultaneously. The heaviest vehicle was in the slow lane right above the hanger, so will have exerted the greatest moment against the balance points. With a total weight of nearly 700 kN, it was clearly enough to destabilize the entire slab, probably fracturing the remaining hanger on the north-east corner, so allowing the whole deck to fall to the river. The photograph of the remains after the accident shows that the large truck left some debris on the far side of the void, probably from the truck cab, which just clipped the edge of the road during its fall (Figure 4.38). Since it was still travelling forward at speed, its final resting position against a bridge pier lay beyond the large hole in the road.

3.5 Accident causes

Determining the sequence of events as shown by the physical remains, however, only opened up further questions about how such corrosion could have occurred over a long period of time without being detected. All bridges were required by law to be

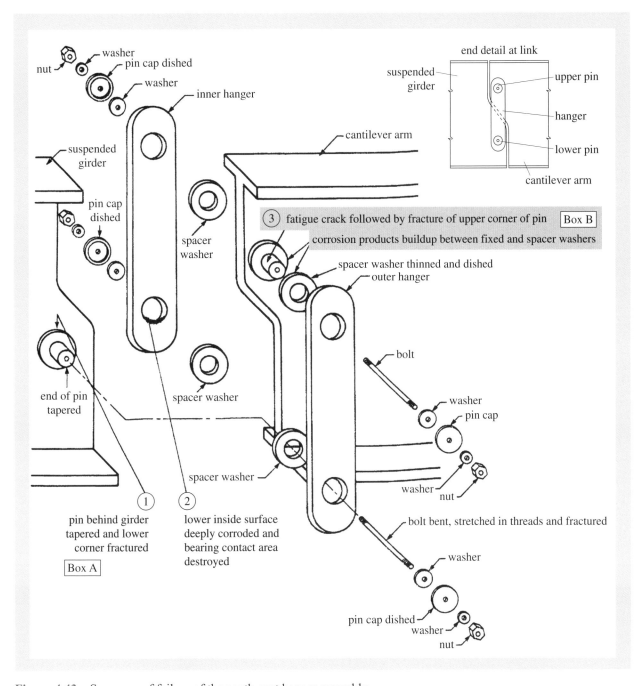

Figure 4.43 Sequence of failure of the south-east hanger assembly

inspected regularly and thoroughly, especially after the Silver Bridge tragedy only 16 years before, so what went wrong?

The investigators found that inspection was difficult. Access to the underside of the bridge was via a catwalk (seen at the left below the road in Figure 4.38), and the hanger assemblies were some distance away at the edge of the structure. Moreover, most of the damage occurred within the bearings and was thus hidden from view. If the maintenance personnel had been able to get close enough to the bearings then they would, however, undoubtedly have spotted the bulging of the plates covering the pins and taken remedial action.

But why were the bearings so susceptible to corrosion? Unprotected steel is of course liable to rust, but presumably it was thought that being under the roadway would shield the bearings from the worst of any rain. However, it was discovered that the main drains at the edges of the highway had been deliberately blocked up and covered over in 1973 as a cost-saving measure, to save cleaning out the drains (Figure 4.44); as a result, water was free to run down through the gaps at the sides and so directly onto the bearings. Direct evidence of flow into the bearings was shown by rust smears either side of the hangers. Water found its way onto the bearings, percolated into them and then was trapped in the cavity between the washers. Rusting occurred there over a long period of time. The corrosion rate will have been high owing to the common practice of salting the road surfaces against frost. Wetted surfaces remain moist for longer, and chloride ions destroy any protective oxide layers.

So a poor maintenance decision had led to the bearings being exposed to corrosion. But there was another design problem: if a single bearing failed then there was nothing to prevent free fall of the deck. The cantilever and the suspended deck were configured in an 'S' shape. If this design had been reversed, however, then the fixed cantilever would have supported the suspended deck even if the bearing failed completely. It would of course have lowered the road surface, but the deck would not have fallen disastrously away. However, the bearings were non-redundant, and this design defect was built into the bridge from the date of construction. The eye-bar links on the suspension chains of the Silver Bridge presented a similar problem: in the event of failure of only one eye bar, the load would inevitably lead to failure of its companions.

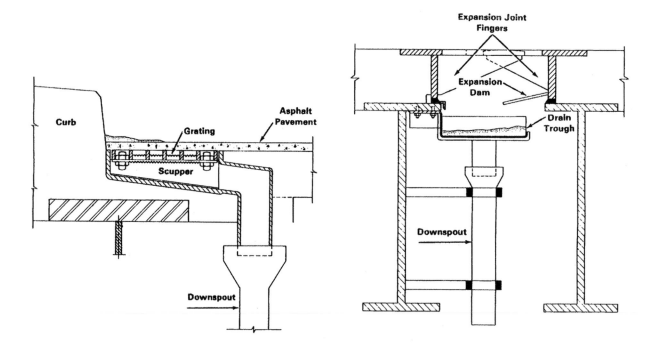

Figure 4.44   Structure of blocked drain

Redundant components in any design are critical parts of a structure, but should failure occur they cannot compromise its integrity. In other suspended bridge designs, for example, each deck was supported by several bearings rather than just two. In the event of total bearing failure, the load would be redistributed and so disaster would be prevented.

Most products where safety of the user is critical will have redundant components. Aircraft, for example, have dual hydraulic circuits so that in the event of failure and loss of pressure in one line, the systems can utilize the second to restore hydraulic power to the working parts such as the ailerons on the wings and tail. Most twin-engined modern aircraft can still fly with only one working engine if the other fails during flight. In effect, redundancy is another aspect of the safety-factor problem, making allowance for failure of critical components in a structure.

3.6 Aftermath

The repercussions of the accident were far-reaching, with renewed calls for stricter safety standards in new bridges and more widespread and intensive inspection of existing bridges, especially those of similar design to the Mianus River bridge. The immediate effects of the failure were serious enough: diversion of traffic with considerable local disruption. The other suspended decks were found to be badly rusted, so effectively most of the bridge had to be reconstructed.

The bridge has been totally rebuilt to an entirely different design; there are now more concrete piers and steel beams running longitudinally along the axis of the roadway (Figure 4.45). In 2005, there was excellent provision for drainage from the road. A plastic drainage pipe can be seen at extreme right, for example, leading down the concrete pier.

Figure 4.45   State of bridge in 2005

SAQ 4.11 (Learning outcomes 4.11 and 4.13)

Describe briefly the sequence of events leading up to catastrophic failure of a single deck of the Mianus River bridge on 28 June 1983. Indicate what design features led to the accident and how corrosion played a critical role in the failure. Point out any parallels with the Silver Bridge tragedy of 1967.

Unlike the Silver Bridge, where there were only a few other bridges of the same design, there were several thousand road bridges built like the Mianus River bridge. As a result of the Mianus bridge findings they were all inspected very closely; most were either entirely rebuilt or were reinforced to provide greater redundancy. The basic design was flawed, and action was needed to prevent further catastrophic failures. However, corrosion can still cause problems today, as the example of the ☑ **Sgt Aubrey Cosens VC Memorial Bridge** ☑ shows.

☑ Sgt Aubrey Cosens VC Memorial Bridge

Rusting of key parts of a bridge continues to create problems for civil engineers, as an example from Canada shows. A partial failure of the Sgt Aubrey Cosens VC Memorial Bridge occurred on 14 January 2003 at approximately 3.00 p.m. The steel arch bridge is located on Highway 11 and spans the Montreal River. As a southbound tractor-trailer crossed the bridge, the concrete deck deflected approximately 2 m at the north-west corner due to the failure of 3 hanger rods (Figure 4.46). The bridge was immediately closed to traffic.

The hangers were connected to the superstructure of the bridge by screwed bolts, and had fractured across the lower threads (Figure 4.47).

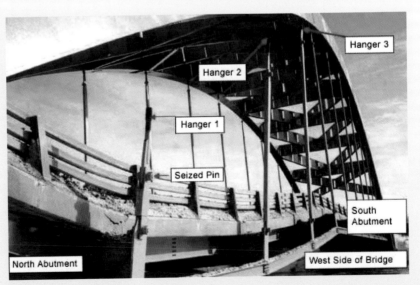

Figure 4.46   Sagging of main deck due to hanger fracture

The fracture surfaces showed all the characteristics of fatigue, with a flat zone preceding the fast fracture zone. The fatigue crack in Hanger 1 started somewhere within the root of the thread at the foot of the slow growth zone (Figure 4.48).

So what was the cause of the fatigue cracks? The lowest part of the hangers were eyes to which the deck of the bridge was attached (Figure 4.46) and, as originally designed, were free to rotate to accommodate movements induced by the live loads of traffic on the bridge. Unfortunately, the eyes had rusted and seized up, placing extra bending loads on the hangers and, ultimately, the bolted top connections.

The bridge was built in 1960, rehabilitated in 1992 and the structural steel painted in 1998. It was the failure of Hanger 3 that led to the final accident; however, Hangers 1 and 2 had failed several years before this, as shown by their rusted surfaces. The extreme cold temperatures (−30 °C) and the quality of the steel used in the hangers also played a role in reducing the ductility of the hangers and accelerating the onset of final fracture. Metallurgical tests confirmed that the hanger material did not remain ductile in temperatures much lower than −18 °C. With steel with a ductile-to-brittle transition temperature of between −18 °C and −29 °C, an overloaded section would experience a brittle fracture at temperatures colder than −18 °C.

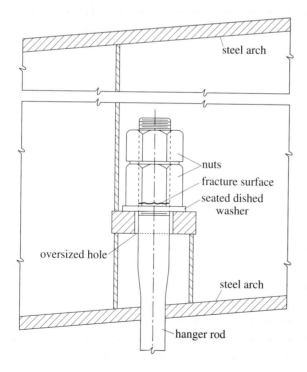

Figure 4.47   Section of hanger connection

Corrosion products around the flat surface of the nut

FFOL: Fast fracture overload zone, 20%

FP: Fatigue propagation zone, 80%

FS: Fracture started somewhere in this area

Figure 4.48   Fracture surface of Hanger 1

4 CASE STUDY 3: THE ALOHA AIRCRAFT ACCIDENT

Stress corrosion cracking affects many different structural materials, although the critical environment will change depending on the materials involved, and the exact circumstances will vary according to the age of the cracking, the age of the structure and its particular environment. Catastrophic bridge failures are bad enough, but the consequences of such failures on aircraft can be even more severe. Sudden loss of safety-critical components, such as part of the fuselage or an engine, could lead to loss of control of the aircraft and disaster if the engines were non-redundant.

The case to be studied here concerns a Hawaiian aircraft that lost part of its fuselage during flight; only by the skill of the pilots and staff was it saved from complete destruction.

4.1 Sequence of events

The accident happened during a routine flight of a rather old Boeing 737 aircraft. The account in this section is based on the official NTSB report.

At 1.25 p.m. on 28 April 1988, flight 243 left Hilo Airport for Honolulu as part of the normal scheduled service. In addition to the two pilots, there were three flight attendants, an air traffic controller and 89 passengers on board. Passenger boarding, engine start, taxi and takeoff were uneventful.

The first officer conducted the takeoff and climb from Hilo. The flight was conducted in good weather.

No unusual occurrences were noted by either pilot during the departure and climb. As the aircraft levelled at 24 000 feet, both pilots heard a loud 'clap' or 'whooshing' sound followed by a wind noise behind them. The first officer's head was jerked backwards, and she stated that debris, including pieces of grey insulation, was floating in the cockpit. The captain observed that the cockpit entry door was missing and that there was blue sky where the first-class ceiling had been. The captain immediately took over the controls of the aircraft. He described the aircraft as rolling slightly left and right and also observed that the flight controls felt 'loose.'

Because of the decompression, both pilots and the air traffic controller in the observer seat put on their oxygen masks. The captain began an emergency descent. He stated that he extended the speed brakes and descended at an indicated airspeed of 280 to 290 knots. Because of ambient noise, the pilots initially used hand signals to communicate. The first officer stated that she observed a rate of descent of 4100 feet per minute at some point during the emergency descent. The captain also stated that he actuated the passenger oxygen switch.

When the decompression occurred, all the passengers were seated and the seatbelt sign was illuminated. The No. 1 flight attendant reportedly was standing at seat row 5. According to the passengers, the flight attendant was immediately swept out of the cabin through a hole in the left side of the fuselage. The No. 2 flight attendant, standing by row 15/16, was thrown to the floor and sustained minor bruises. She was subsequently able to crawl up and down the aisle to render assistance and calm the passengers. The No. 3 flight attendant, standing at row 2, was struck on the head by debris and thrown to the floor. She suffered serious injuries including a concussion and severe head lacerations.

When the aircraft had descended through 14 000 feet, the first officer switched the radio to the Maui Tower frequency. At 1.48 p.m., she informed the tower of the rapid decompression, declared an emergency and stated the need for emergency equipment. Maui Tower acknowledged and began emergency notifications based on the first officer's report of decompression. Rescue vehicles took up alert positions along the left side of the runway.

A normal descent profile was established 4 miles out on the final approach, although the aircraft had by then lost power from one of the engines. The captain said that the aircraft was 'shaking a little, rocking slightly and felt springy'.

Flight 243 landed on runway 02 at Maui's Kahului Airport at 1.58 p.m. The captain said that he was able to make a normal touchdown. He used the No. 2 engine thrust reverser and brakes to stop the aircraft. An emergency evacuation was then accomplished on the runway.

After the accident, a passenger stated that as she was boarding the aircraft through the passenger bridge at Hilo, she observed a longitudinal fuselage crack. The crack was in the upper row of rivets along a lap joint near the cabin door. She made no mention of the observation to the airline ground personnel or flight crew.

Of the total complement of 95, one member of the cabin crew had died and another was seriously injured. No passengers were killed, but 57 suffered injuries of varying severity.

A major portion of the upper crown skin and structure had separated in flight, causing an explosive decompression of the cabin. The damaged area extended from behind the main cabin entrance door, rearward about 18 feet to the area just forward of the wings and from the left side of the cabin at the floor level to the right side window level.

As photographs taken just after the plane landed show (Figure 4.49), the fuselage had been ripped away behind the cabin to such an extent that it was miraculous that the plane made it home safely with so few casualties.

Figure 4.49   The Aloha incident: fuselage immediately after landing

The value of the aircraft was estimated at about $5 million. As a result of the accident, the aircraft was judged to be damaged beyond repair. It was dismantled on the site and sold for parts and scrap.

4.2 Aircraft structure

The fuselage of an aircraft is subjected to stresses similar to those experienced by boilers, and can be regarded as a simple cylindrical pressure vessel with two types of stress in the skin: longitudinal and hoop stresses, the latter being twice as large as the former. Since the hoop stress acts around the diameter of the cylinder, cracks tend to be longitudinal and run along the major axis of the fuselage.

The crack seen by the passenger when boarding the aircraft was a longitudinal crack, and examination of the aircraft after the accident showed that such cracks were present over many parts of the front fuselage. But how had they occurred? Each ascent to high altitudes would put the fuselage under internal pressure, since the pressure inside the cabin must be maintained at a reasonably high level for the occupants. Conversely, the pressure would drop to ambient when the aircraft descended. After the Comet crashes of the early 1950s (which were discussed in Part 2), it was known that cyclical changes in skin stress could initiate fatigue cracks. In the Comet disasters, explosive decompression was caused by fatigue crack growth from cut-outs in the Comet fuselage, such as square-shaped windows.

> **EXERCISE 4.8**
>
> Suggest why fatigue cracks grew from cut-outs in the body.

In the case of the Comet, the problem was exacerbated by the thin aluminium skin forming the fuselage, and by cracks induced by poor manufacturing during the original construction of the aircraft. The problem was overcome eventually by rounding off sharp corners in the cut-outs and by improving the manufacturing methods used in building the fuselage.

So the fuselage of the Boeing 737 involved in the Aloha flight should have had a tough skin, resistant to pressure cycling during flight. Another mechanism was needed to explain why fatigue cracks could be initiated at so many different points in the front fuselage.

4.2.1 Fuselage structure

The body of the plane consisted of a space frame of aluminium alloy beams, to which was riveted a thin aluminium alloy skin; this form of construction had been greatly improved since the Comet pioneered the structure in the 1950s. The main beams included circumferential frames, which divided the fuselage into four major sections, and stringers, which were horizontal beams running along the length of the body (Figure 4.50). The former were of Z-section, while the latter were of a top-hat section to maximize stiffness.

The complex way in which the parts were assembled was designed to achieve several aims, including structural integrity, allowance for fail-safety and ease of manufacture

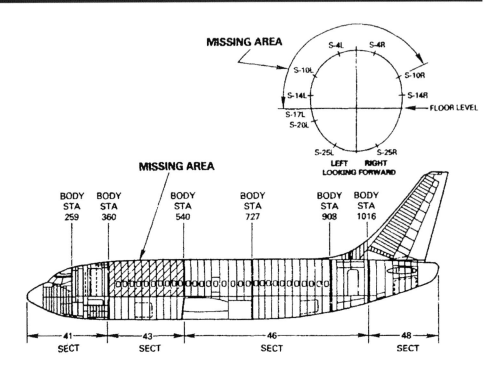

Figure 4.50 Structure of Boeing 737, showing the four major sections of the fuselage

on the production line. A typical section is shown in Figure 4.51(a), in an expanded three-dimensional form so as to highlight details. The skin is formed from 0.9 mm thick sheet, and the rectangular panels, about 4 by 2 metres in size, are joined by three lines of rivets where they overlap (Figure 4.51b). The structure incorporates so-called 'tear straps', which are fail-safe devices intended to fail first to allow cabin air to escape in the event of fuselage overload.

4.2.2 Epoxy scrim

During assembly of the airframe, the lap joint is formed by attaching a cold-cure epoxy scrim to one of the cleaned surfaces of the panels to be joined (Figure 4.51c), which are then brought together under pressure as the epoxy thin film cures (or cross-links). The epoxy resin used is a 'one-pot' epoxy, unlike the two-pot resins commonly supplied to householders to mend broken products. Several problems had been found when using one-pot epoxy adhesive in airframe construction. Because it cures at room temperature, it must be stored at a low temperature, typically at the temperature of solid CO_2 or dry ice (-78.5 °C). Any moisture in the atmosphere will initiate curing, so it should also be kept very dry. Being very cold when applied could induce water condensation, and prevent a good bond with the underlying oxide film on the metal surface. If too warm, it could also spontaneously cross-link, again preventing a good bond with the airframe.

> Two-pot resins are supplied in two separate tubes: they are mixed just before applying to the surfaces to be joined, which are then pressured while the resin cures. Araldite® is one such proprietary epoxy available to homeowners.

Whatever the source of the problem, it was discovered that bonding could be very variable on finished aircraft, with some parts bonding well, and others not at all or only poorly. Since the frame had been designed with the assumption of good bonding, the integrity of the frame would be compromised in those areas affected by poor bonding of the scrim.

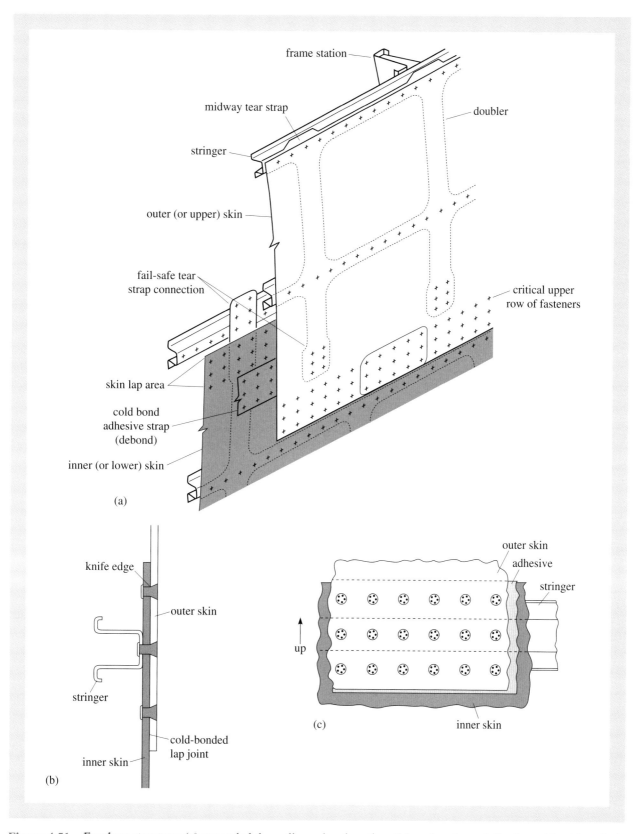

Figure 4.51 Fuselage structure: (a) expanded three-dimensional section; (b) section through fuselage skin; (c) typical lap bond

There had been several warning incidents before the Aloha accident, indicating that there was a problem with the scrim on Boeing 737s. If there was no bond with the scrim, then there would be a small gap at the edge of the outer lap joint. Such a gap, however slight, would attract liquid water by capillary action ('water wicking'). Corrosion could then occur in the joint, especially if there were traces of salt present.

Such internal pressure from the expansion owing to corrosion products could allow the hoop stresses that arose during pressure flights to be transferred to the line of rivets. This unexpected loading could give rise to fatigue cracking. However, it was first necessary to determine what the surviving evidence of the Aloha incident actually showed.

4.3 The investigation

The investigation by the NTSB revealed that the aircraft was relatively old, having been with Aloha Airlines since 1969, shortly after its manufacture. By the time of the accident it had accumulated 35 496 flight hours and no fewer than 89 680 flight cycles, mainly because it was used for short trips between the islands. As a direct result, it had not achieved full pressurization of 50 kPa during every cycle. It had the second highest number of flight cycles in the worldwide 737 fleet.

4.3.1 Extent of damage

As is normal in such reports, one of the first tasks was to summarize the location and nature of the damage to both the frame and the internal components. With such extensive loss of the frame and much of the fuselage missing (and never recovered from the sea), the investigators would have to concentrate on the remains still attached to the aircraft. Although critical parts might be missing, enough might survive for the failure sequence to be inferred. Investigators would concentrate on identifying brittle cracks and distinguishing damage caused after the first event (rather than before), indicating overload or ductile behaviour.

The pictures taken after landing show that almost half the section aft of the cabin had disappeared (Figure 4.49). Examination of the surrounding zones revealed the following damage:

1   skin peeling from the frame (visible on the lower section below the passengers in Figure 4.49) on both sides of the craft

2   circumferential break at body station (BS) 360 (see Figure 4.50) with skin pulled through rivet heads in an aft direction, with fracture and deformation of stringers

3   circumferential break at BS 540 (left side) from the top of the plane, with the upper half not associated with any rivet line; from the S–10L lap joint (Figure 4.50, upper right), fracture followed the upper line of rivets with fatigue cracks at seven consecutive rivets

4   circumferential break at BS 540 (right side) from the top of the plane to the S–10R lap joint, with broken stringers and skin pulled through rivets showing that the separated structure was pulled forward.

So early inspection showed that the two types of evidence could easily be distinguished, suggesting a possible sequence of events.

The most important observation concerned the fatigue cracks along the lines of rivets. They were found at several points in the remains, especially concentrated at the rear part of the gap in the fuselage. There were three zones: S–10L lap joint ahead of the BS 540 break, on each side of a rivet hole in the BS 360 butt strap near S–7R, and in a lap joint recovered from the right wing. All other fractures had been created by overload, showing ductile tearing.

The fracture surfaces surrounding the separation perimeter were corrosion-free. Corrosion damage, including debonded areas, was found, however, in the butt joints at BS 360 and BS 540. There were also some areas of bulged skin on the intact lap joints and circumferential butt joints remaining on the plane.

Other internal damage was observed, as one would expect from such a traumatic event. There was impact damage on the leading edges of both wings, and numerous dents on the stabilizers. The inlet cowls of both engines were dented, and several first-stage fan blades at the front of the aircraft were damaged. Some control-line cables had also been damaged near the engines. Heavy corrosion was found in areas of separation of the cables. There was extensive damage to wire bundles near the cabin, and circuit breakers here had been tripped.

Internal floors in the separation zone had been heavily damaged. Five consecutive floor beams between BS 360 and BS 540 had fractured through their centres, and adjacent floor beams were nearly cracked through. Extensive displacement of the floor panels had occurred in the separation zone, but fortunately the cabin was undamaged. A fuselage section from between S–4R and S–8R was trapped between the leading edge flap and the inboard side of the right engine strut, the only piece of the lost fuselage to be recovered. It contained two skin repairs along S–4R. This piece of fuselage was analysed further by the NTSB Materials Laboratory.

4.3.2 Material examination

Several samples were examined by the Materials Laboratory, including the piece from the missing fuselage caught by the right wing. The latter had been repaired in the form of two doubler patches covering several rivet lines. When removed, they revealed extensive fatigue cracking in the upper row of rivets both under and between the patches, including the longest crack found anywhere on the aircraft: 5.25 mm long. This stringer section (S–4R) contained three areas where the fail-safe tear straps had been riveted above the primary lap joint (Figure 4.51a), and there was extensive fatigue cracking in all three zones. The entire cold-bonded lap joint had become debonded, with corrosion varying from light to severe here, including irreparable metal depletion.

The lap joint samples S–4L from BS 727 to 747 and from BS 847 to 867 each possessed 18 columns of lap-joint rivets. Fatigue cracks extended from the lateral edges of virtually every rivet hole in the upper rows (Figure 4.52), with the longer cracks about halfway between the tear straps.

The final piece examined was S–4L from BS 519 to 536. It showed fatigue cracks from 16 consecutive rivet holes along the upper row of the lap joint. The longest such crack measured 4.6 mm from the knife edge of the countersunk hole (Figure 4.53). Debonding was present in both this area and the adjacent tear-strap zones. Light to moderate corrosion was present between the aluminium sheets.

Figure 4.52 Schematic showing multiple crack formation in upper rivet row of lap joint

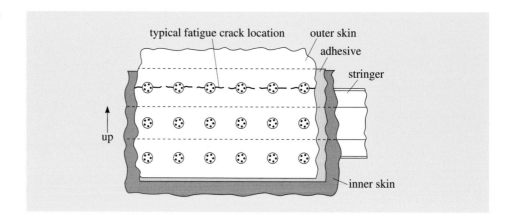

Figure 4.53 Section through rivet showing morphology of typical fatigue crack from Aloha accident

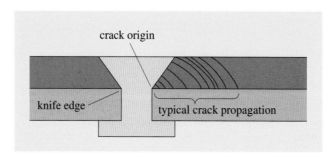

Since the investigators had observed highly distinct fatigue fracture surfaces, they could count the number of striations on the surfaces. The results from several samples are shown in Table 4.3. A clear correlation was found between crack length and striation counts, a reasonable observation since each striation represents a single cycle of load when the crack extends by a minute amount. The highest numbers and longest cracks are the oldest, and may be compared with the total flight cycle history of nearly 90 000 cycles. Although the number of cycles for each crack is substantially lower than the total number of flight cycles, this is not entirely unexpected; fatigue initiation and growth was the final event in a longer failure sequence, starting with debonding of the lap joint, followed by corrosion within the crevice and the resulting internal pressure exerted by the increased volume of the hydrated oxide.

Table 4.3 Striation counts on Aloha fuselage samples

Specimen location	Estimated number of cycles (±20%)	Crack length/mm
S–4R	28 670	2.67
S–4R	37 148	3.30
S–4R	28 656	3.61
S–4R	26 449	3.91
S–4R	24 056	2.79
S–10L	23 628	4.09
S–10L	36 379	3.68

Source: National Transportation Safety Board (1989)

The critical crack, which would have shown the largest striation count, was presumably lost with the bulk of the absent fuselage skin.

> ### SAQ 4.12 (Learning outcomes 4.6 and 4.10)
>
> Describe the stresses arising in the skin of an aircraft fuselage, and relate these stresses to the wall thickness, the diameter of the fuselage and the pressure differential between internal and external pressures.
>
> Explain why the fatigue cracks started at the sharp countersunk corner of the rivet heads in the upper row in Figure 4.52.

The same inspection revealed other locations of fatigue cracking. Circumferential fatigue cracks were found in a butt-strap section either side of a rivet hole. In addition, corrosion had affected cable control wires for the engines, but the exact type and cause of the problem are not discussed further in the official report.

4.4 Failure sequence

The body of evidence was now sufficient to suggest the sequence of events in the accident. The critical crack had been lost when the upper part of the front fuselage was lost during explosive decompression. No parts were discovered in the extensive air and sea search after the accident.

Inspection of the remains after the plane had landed showed that much of the damage was ductile in nature, especially at the forward end of the affected section (Figures 4.49 and 4.50). The circumferential frames at either end of the section were intact. The appearance of the damage, concentrated on the left-hand side of the plane, suggested that decompression started there rather than on the right-hand side. Damage to the cabin floor was also greatest there. (Similar damage had been seen in a Turkish Airlines DC-10 crash in France in 1974, when a cargo door floor was suddenly lost. The damage to the floor was concentrated near the cargo door itself.)

The locus of such damage suggested that the skin failed first midway in the section, at one of the upper lap joints S–10L or S–14L. Had it occurred at S–14L, it would have been below the window line and there would have been insufficient wall to react to pressure inside the cabin to have produced the visible damage. The NTSB thus concluded that failure started at lap joint S–10L.

This conclusion was supported by evidence of extensive fatigue cracking on seven adjacent upper rivet holes in the remaining part of this lap joint found on the remains. In addition, a passenger had seen a skin crack near a top row of rivets in S–10L at the cabin door (verified later by showing the witness another identical aircraft). The passengers also reported that the missing flight attendant was in the aisle at seat 5, close to S–10L near BS 440.

So why had the tear straps failed to allow controlled decompression? The problem lay in debonding of the epoxy layer. If this occurs, then the tear straps are ineffective because stiffening is lost, and the cracks grow as if the tear straps are not there.

Catastrophic failure occurred when the fatigue cracks in the top row of rivets on lap joint S–10L joined up to form a giant crack that then grew uncontrollably.

Corrosion in the debonded areas of the lap joints exacerbated failure by increasing the degree of separation between the two sheets forming the overlap. The pressure exerted by the expanding deposit would have encouraged further debonding if, for example, the epoxy bond was weak but still holding the joint together. Water entering the joint may also have encouraged debonding. If the capillary water froze, then further debonding may have occurred by the expansion of the ice (the freeze–thaw effect).

SAQ 4.13 (Learning outcome 4.2)

(a) Explain why corrosion of the aluminium skin of the Aloha aircraft started in the crevice between the two separate sheets following loss of bonding between them.

(b) Given that the density of hydrated aluminium oxide ($Al_2O_3.3H_2O$) is 2.42 g cm^{-3}, compared with a metal density of 2.702 g cm^{-3}, what effect would corrosion have on the stresses at the joint?

(c) What local environmental factors were important in the development of the corrosion problem with flight 243?

4.5 Aftermath

As the known facts about the problem with debonding became available, there was some pressure on Aloha Airlines to reveal their inspection records and procedures, especially after it was known that a passenger observed cracks while boarding flight 243. The problem of debonding was well known to Boeing, who had issued several warnings to all airlines operating 737s worldwide. Although they had recommended inspection for fatigue cracks using an eddy current method, the resolution of the method fell below expectations. The fatigue cracks would have been invisible at the start of their growth, since they were initiated at the sharp rivet edge below the skin surface; they would have been difficult to see even when they emerged on the outer surface. However, hairline cracking was an old and well-known problem with aluminium airframes, so Aloha should have been extra vigilant in their inspections, especially after the warnings from Boeing. That they failed to detect the problem and rectify the situation was found by the NTSB to be a primary cause of the catastrophic incident on flight 243.

Other Boeing 737 aircraft in the Aloha fleet were inspected by the NTSB for debonding, corrosion and fatigue. Several were found to be in such a serious state that they were immediately scrapped.

More information on the debonding problem emerged during the inquiry. There had been a previous accident involving debonding, corrosion and fatigue cracking of the fuselage of a Boeing 737 on 22 August 1981 in Taiwan. In that instance the plane had not survived the catastrophic decompression, and all 110 people on board died. The Chinese Civil Airline Authority found that the disaster had been caused by extensive corrosion in the lower fuselage structure. The plane had experienced 33 313 flight cycles at the time of the accident and the explosive decompression caused mid-air break-up.

The passengers and crew of Aloha flight 243 were very lucky not to have suffered the same fate.

SAQ 4.14 (Learning outcomes 4.10 and 4.13)

Describe the sequence of events that led to the accident on Aloha flight 243. Include explanation of the phenomena involved and the role corrosion played in the final accident, discussing the evidence on which your argument is based.

5 DETERIORATION OF NON-METALLIC MATERIALS

It is not just metals and alloys that deteriorate. Polymers are a large class of structural materials whose properties can change with time. Natural materials, especially textiles and wood, deteriorate rapidly under the right conditions. This usually occurs through the action of micro-organisms that recycle the elements of which the materials are composed into food that can be easily absorbed by other living things.

Oxidation is also an important mechanism of chain degradation in polymers, owing to the ubiquitous presence of oxygen in the atmosphere and the use of powerful oxidizing agents, such as chlorine, in cleaning products for their anti-bacterial properties. Also, radiation in the form of ultraviolet rays in sunshine can be energetic enough to degrade the chains of many polymeric materials.

Heat alone will, of course, melt materials when the crystal melting point is reached. In polymers, however, there is an additional risk of *thermal degradation*, below the melting point, which usually breaks chains and lowers the strength of polymeric materials.

5.1 Fuel-line failure

Chemical attack of polymers occurs when they interact with aggressive chemicals, some of which I have already mentioned in the context of metal corrosion. Again, as with metals, sometimes only tiny amounts of attacking reagent are needed to initiate degradation in the form of brittle cracks. Propagation usually occurs if the part is tensioned, but residual stress or ☑ **frozen-in strain** ☑ can be enough to encourage crack growth.

As with stress corrosion cracking of metals, attack can be rapid and produce totally unexpected effects, sometimes with tragic results and often involving property damage.

☑ Frozen-in strain

When polymers are formed by methods such as injection moulding, the flow of the liquid polymer into the mould can cause the polymer chains to be aligned by a shear process. This can be demonstrated by viewing a plastic ruler, for example, between crossed polarizing filters (Figure 4.54), as seen in the photoelasticity experiments described in Block 1 and on the DVD.

The colours in Figure 4.54(a) are a result of the birefringence of the aligned polymer molecules. Now, you might suspect that this indicates a stress, as we saw for photoelastic measurement, but we can demonstrate that this isn't the case by making a saw cut in the ruler, as shown in Figure 4.54(b). If there were a stress present, the cut would cause it to relax around the cut surfaces; however, there is ▷

no change in the fringe pattern at all. The fringes are present because the polymer chains were aligned during injection moulding, but there is no residual stress involved in keeping them aligned.

However, the equilibrium condition for the polymer chains is for them to become more jumbled and random. Heating the ruler to above the *glass-transition temperature* of the polymer causes this to happen. The chains become more mobile: there are no longer any fringes present in the ruler (Figure 4.54c), as the polymer chains are no longer aligned; and the ruler has distorted considerably, owing to the relaxation of the polymer molecules.

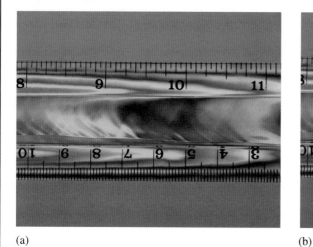

(a)

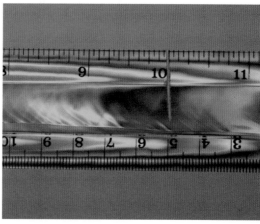

(b)

(c)

Figure 4.54   (a) The fringes in a polymer ruler; (b) no change to the fringes when the ruler is cut; (c) what happens when the ruler is heated

5.1.1 Car accident

The failure of fuel lines can have disastrous consequences simply because fuel is volatile and highly inflammable. Car fires, for example, are relatively common events, even in new cars, and are often caused by fuel-line failure. If a line is punctured, a spray of fuel is easily ignited under the bonnet of a car by the many sources of ignition nearby. A vapour cloud produces an explosion, especially in petrol-driven vehicles, where the fuel is highly volatile.

Diesel fuel is less easily ignited, but leaks can give dangerous results if the fuel drops into the road. When the light fractions have evaporated, diesel leaves a very greasy deposit, equivalent to black ice in lubricity. Like black ice, this deposit is difficult for drivers to spot. For example, in Scotland in 1996 a vehicle developed a leak in a diesel return pipe that caused no fewer than four accidents to following cars. The most serious accident was a head-on collision when a driver skidded on the spilt diesel and veered into the oncoming lane. She was very seriously injured, and remained in intensive care for months.

> Return pipes are part of the fuel circulation system in diesel engines, where excess fuel is returned to the tank.

5.1.2 The failed pipe

So what caused the diesel spill? The police followed the trail of fuel to a vehicle with a split fuel pipe (Figure 4.55), and the Forensic Science Service attributed the failure to vandalism. Apparently, someone had cut the pipe transversely with a knife.

However, the pipe itself was buried deep within the engine compartment, so was inaccessible to any vandal. The cut end needed closer inspection to determine how it had failed. In fact, it turned out not to be the plastic pipe that had failed, but rather a plastic connector, attached by shrink-fit joints. Analysis showed that the pipe was extruded from nylon 12, while the connector had been moulded in nylon 6,6: see ☑ **Grades of nylon** ☑.

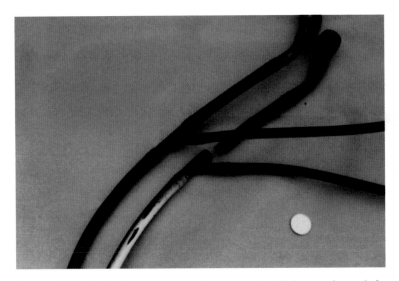

Figure 4.55   Failed fuel pipe at right compared with intact pipe at left

▽ Grades of nylon

The distinction between nylon 12 and nylon 6,6 lies in the arrangement of atoms in the polymer chain; both have a so-called 'amide' group ($-CO-NH-$) in the backbone of the polymer chains, but whereas the former has a polyethylene chain of 11 methylene units ($-CH_2-$) between each amide group, the latter has a group of 4 or 6 methylene units. The change in structure has quite dramatic effects on the properties of the nylon. Nylon 12 melts at a much lower temperature of about 180 °C, compared with nylon 6,6 which melts at about 260 °C. Nylon 12 is also less crystalline, because there are fewer amide bonds to link together in the crystallites, and thus has a lower modulus, making tubing more flexible than its nylon 6,6 equivalent. Both nylons are highly resistant to fuels, whether petrol or diesel, so nylon 12 is widely used in fuel lines. Both are also very tough materials, and fail when strained in a ductile fashion, with yielding and extension. △

The fracture surface of the failed end proved that the pipe had not been cut. A cut produces characteristic lines parallel to the movement of the blade from tiny defects in the edge, but no such marks could be seen in the failed surface (Figure 4.56). a component had fractured in a brittle way and there were many features that indicated slow progressive crack growth. They included:

- an eroded outer edge

- a small longitudinal crack

- several striations across the surface

- a ductile cusp furthest away from the eroded edge.

So what had caused the failure? One way to solve this problem was to examine the elemental distribution over the surface using the X-ray analysis facility on a scanning electron microscope. This would also yield a more detailed picture of the surface itself. Figure 4.57, for example, shows the cusp end of the surface, with many very fine striations within the larger ones visible in the optical microscope.

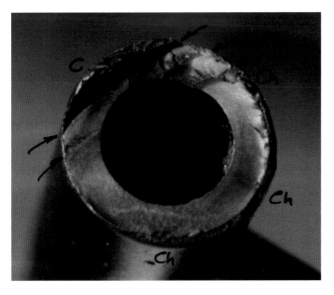

Figure 4.56 Fracture surface of connector, taken with an optical microscope

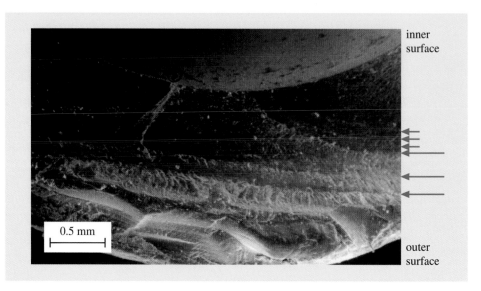

Figure 4.57   Environmental scanning electron microscopy (ESEM) image showing detail of fracture: the long arrows mark larger striations, while the short arrows mark the finer ones

The striations probably represent successive positions of a slowly growing brittle crack (Figure 4.58). It was unusual for the nylon 6,6 to show a brittle failure, however. Fatigue was one possible explanation, because the failure had probably started from the corner of the connection with the nylon 12 fuel pipe. However, it did not appear to be a very serious stress concentrator, so something else had been involved in initiating the crack.

X-ray analysis showed the expected presence of carbon, hydrogen and nitrogen, together with some minor impurities. The most important of these was sulphur, especially in the region of the fracture furthest away from the cusp.

Sulphur was an unusual element to find on the surface, because it would not be present in the fuel owing to its poisoning effect during refining. It is not present in grease either, which is a contaminant one might expect to find in the confines of an engine compartment.

The only common fluid in a car engine in which sulphur is found is sulphuric acid, H_2SO_4, which is used as an electrolyte in car batteries. In a fully charged battery it is present at a 40% concentration. However, it is fully confined within the plastic battery case, so its presence on a fuel line is unusual.

The edge furthest from the ductile cusp (Figure 4.58) showed signs of attack by an aggressive reagent, with erosion of the corner, which might explain the failure. But what chemicals could cause such erosion? Nylons possess amide groups, which are susceptible to attack from acids – it is well known that spills of acids will attack clothing, for example – so here lay the kernel of a possible explanation of the problem.

Figure 4.59 shows the loss in tenacity (a measure of the strength of fibres) for two synthetic polymers, nylon 6,6 and polyester, over a range of temperatures. The curves are for exposure to dilute sulphuric acid, and show how quickly and badly nylon is affected compared to polyester materials. Nylon 6,6 is clearly very sensitive to acid attack, which causes hydrolysis of the chain molecules. The strength drops very rapidly for even small changes in chain length (or molecular weight).

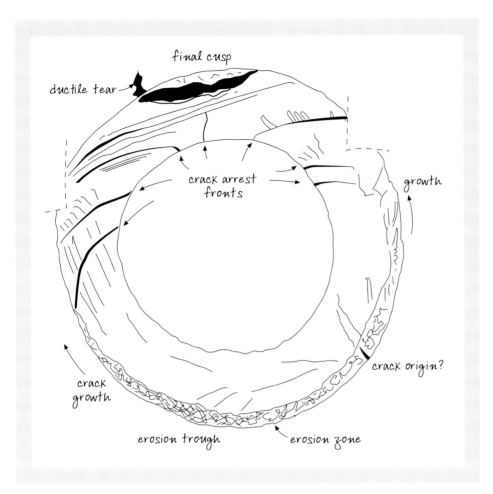

Figure 4.58   Fracture surface map: the dashed lines mark regions where insufficient data was available

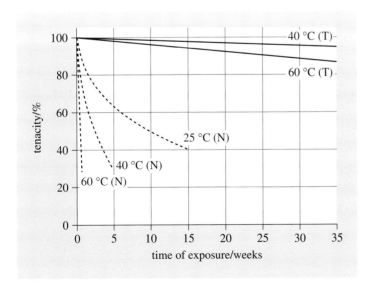

Figure 4.59   Hydrolysis of nylon 6,6 (N) and polyester (T) by sulphuric acid

It is plausible that the connector was attacked by sulphuric acid leaking from the vehicle battery, which eroded the nylon 6,6 and subsequently led to brittle cracking across the sample. But by the time the investigator developed this hypothesis, over two years after the accident, the battery had been replaced; so the theory could not be corroborated. However, battery leaks are not uncommon, owing to brittle cracks that develop in the low-grade polypropylene cases. Indeed, the investigator himself had suffered a battery leak in his own car that corroded the vehicle frame below the battery. The defect lay undiscovered until the loss of electrolyte was so severe as to render the battery defunct. The source of the problem was revealed only when the battery was replaced.

In the accident vehicle, the return pipe lay directly below the battery and it is likely that a small leak of acid fell onto the connector, initiating the crack. In a trial experiment, a new connector exposed to 40% sulphuric acid cracked in a brittle fashion within 24 hours, despite being only lightly loaded. (Nylon 12 tubing showed no attack whatsoever.) In this test, the crack grew because of residual strain in the injection moulding and due to the (very low) self-weight of the sample in what was an entirely static situation. The accident crack, however, was not immersed in battery acid; once the small drop of acid had been exhausted, attack would no longer occur. So how long did the actual crack on the vehicle take to grow to a critical size?

5.1.3 Failure sequence

The main crack surface showed 7 major striations with numerous much finer striations within them. To postulate how they grew, it was necessary to examine how the return pipe was loaded in service. The connector was attached to flexible nylon 12 tubing leading to fixed fuel ports on the engine manifold, and apparently to another fixture in the engine compartment by a strap (judging by a scrap vehicle of the same design inspected after the accident). However, it was otherwise free to move within bounds limited only by the length and flexibility of the tubing. This effectively meant that there was little stress on the connector, apart from vibrations transmitted from the engine itself.

However, once the stress corrosion crack had been created, even low imposed loads would stimulate crack growth – vibrations from the engine probably led to the final failure of the connector. The vehicle involved was a garage recovery vehicle, and it is normal for such vehicles to be started in the morning and left running during the working day. The largest load would, therefore, have occurred on start-up, succeeded by smaller loads during acceleration of the engine, and the pipe would have been most susceptible to any bending loads it experienced (since these are the most severe).

So the largest striations were associated with starting the engine, the finest with acceleration phases. If there were 7 striations, then there were 7 starts, with the sequence lasting about a week. But the first major striation occurs well over halfway down the fracture surface and there will have been some leakage of fuel during that time. It may have been a small leak initially, because the joint was held together by the remainder of the material, with fuel escaping through the edges of the brittle crack. As the internal pressure is only 20–40 kPa, the leak would not have been serious enough to be noticeable through loss of fuel. However, the investigation determined that a careful driver should have spotted drips from the chassis, becoming more frequent as the crack grew larger with time. The final separation probably occurred when driving, and then much larger amounts of fuel gushed out onto the road.

The driver seriously injured in the head-on collision was awarded substantial compensation as a result of the investigation.

SAQ 4.15 (Learning outcomes 4.11 and 4.13)

What was the sequence of events that led to a serious accident involving diesel fuel spillage onto a road surface? Indicate what defects were found in the pipe and how they arose.

5.2 Ozone attack

Oxidation is a universal fact of life for structural materials, which usually require some form of protection or inhibition. The high oxygen content of the atmosphere means that the gas is present in all exposed locations, being absent only in enclosed situations (where the oxygen may be depleted by corrosion, for example). Another, highly aggressive form of the element is known as ozone, in which three oxygen atoms are linked together to form a single molecule, O_3. Ozone is gaseous under normal temperatures and pressures.

High energies are needed to make ozone (typically ultraviolet radiation and electrical discharge). It is formed naturally in the stratosphere, many miles above the earth's surface, by short-wavelength UV radiation present in the sun's rays. This reaction prevents some of that energetic radiation from reaching the surface of the earth. But ozone can also be formed when other (mainly organic) molecules are present. Exhaust fumes from internal combustion vehicles can promote the formation of ozone in a dangerous condition known as photochemical smog, which is a hazard of many cities – Los Angeles and Mexico City being two well-known examples. The conditions needed for such smogs include bright sunshine and heavy vehicle pollution.

Ozone is also created during thunderstorms by the passage of lightning through the air, and in any electrical discharge associated with equipment. This includes not just sparking but also silent electrical discharge, where electrons bleed away from a surface such as in photocopying. Sparking is common in motor generators, so ozone levels will be high near working equipment.

5.2.1 Ozone cracking

Ozone attacks many materials, but especially rubbers containing double bonds (as in the group –CH=CH–) in the polymer chain. This includes natural rubber, and the synthetics polybutadiene and styrene–butadiene rubber (SBR), all of which contain a double bond at every repeat unit. The ozone gas reacts with the double bond very quickly, cleaving the chain, in what is known as the chain scission equation:

$$-CH=CH- + O_3 \rightarrow -CH=O + -CO_2H$$

The rubber will develop a crack if under tension, because the material will shrink away from the break, exposing fresh rubber to gas attack. Only a very modest

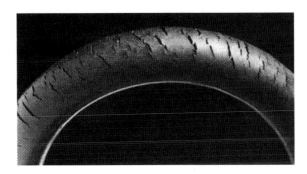

Figure 4.60   Ozone cracking in bent, natural rubber tube

tensile strain of about 1% is needed for crack growth, in comparison with the normal reversible strain for rubbers of up to about 800%. Gas concentrations of 5 parts per million are sufficient to cause rapid attack, but even lower concentrations will attack sensitized materials. Attack is also cumulative, since once cracking has started it cannot be reversed. Figure 4.60 shows ozone cracks in a bent rubber tube, where the cracks have grown at right angles to the applied strain.

Ozone cracking in engineered products such as tyres used to be common – tyre sidewalls typically suffered deep cracking. However, anti-ozonants are now added to inhibit attack, so the problem is rarely seen except in very old or reject tyres. Since tyres are also replaced when the tread has been worn down by a few millimetres, they are rarely aged sufficiently for cracks to be observed. This is true of many other rubber products, although common disposables like rubber bands will experience the problem if left under even a slight tension near an ozone source. Rubber bands can be used for detecting ozone, such is the sensitivity of natural rubber to the gas.

5.2.2 Critical seal failure

Rubber seals are widely used in pneumatic equipment, where pressurized air at about 55 kPa is used to operate doors on trains and buses, for example. Pneumatic systems require numerous rubber seals to prevent leakage of the air to the atmosphere. A variety of different elastomers are used, including nitrile–butadiene rubber (NBR) and polyurethane.

Perhaps the most well-known failure of a rubber seal was the ☒ **Challenger disaster** ☒.

☒ Challenger disaster

Temperature can affect the properties of elastomers in critical ways, just as with other materials. The failure of two large O-rings on the booster rocket for the Challenger lift-off on the morning of 28 January 1986 caused the loss of 8 lives and was a major setback for NASA. It was a totally preventable accident because the problem was well known at Thiokol Corp, the manufacturer of the booster rocket, as well as at NASA itself. The rings were internal seals on several stages of the rocket (Figure 4.61), designed to contain the explosive, burning contents.

Large internal pressures are generated in the metal casing, tending to bend the joint outwards; the inner side of the split joint bends the opposite way, so opening a gap that the expanding gases can penetrate. The inner part of the joint is   ▷

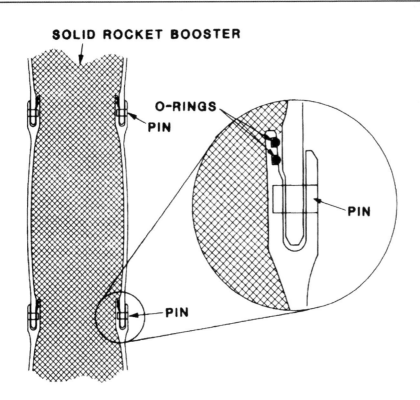

Figure 4.61   O-rings on the booster rocket

thus fitted with two O-rings made from a heat-resistant elastomer known as Viton®. This is a material made using fluorinated rubber, not dissimilar to PTFE in structure if not physical properties. However, if the O-rings cannot respond in time to the bending loads, then they will be eroded and eventually the hot booster gases will leave the casing.

This was a well-known problem before the launch of Challenger. So what could cause a loss of response in the O-rings? The weather before and approaching the launch was unusually cold for Florida; the air temperature dropped below 0 °C and icicles formed over much of the equipment. Lowered temperature was one way in which the elasticity of the rubber could fall. Figure 4.62 shows the way in which lowering the temperature lowers the rate of response

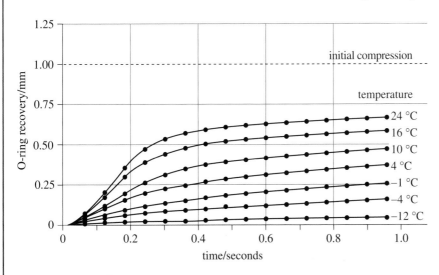

Figure 4.62   O-ring recovery vs time

of the compressed rings; even modestly low temperatures, near freezing, drastically affect the rate at which the rings could expand to fill the gap in the joint.

However, despite the low temperature it was decided to proceed with the launch; the gases escaped from a gap formed in the booster rocket, causing the disaster (Figure 4.63).

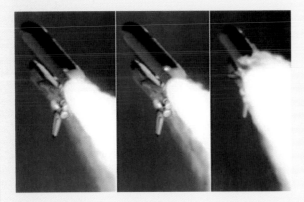

Figure 4.63   Gas escaping from the booster rocket in the Challenger disaster

More sophisticated pneumatic circuits are also used during fabrication of semiconductor chips, where the pressurized air works access ports, handling tools and, most important, the air bearings needed to support the tables on which the chips are etched and coated.

A problem arose on a bank of such chip-etching machines in Japan, where production was halted when the air bearings suddenly failed to operate correctly. The etching table is supported by the air pressure in the chamber below, which is separated from the general air supply by a seal that is in turn supported by a thin, steel diaphragm fitted with a rubber seal. There is a small pressure differential between the chamber and the air supply, which must be maintained to keep the table stable. If the chamber pressure is lost, the table moves out of register, and chip manipulation is no longer possible.

The fault was traced to cracked nitrile–butadiene rubber (NBR) seals in the air bearings. NBR contains butadiene and nitrile repeat units:

Butadiene repeat unit $-[CH_2-CH=CH-CH]-$
Nitrile repeat unit $-[CH_2-CH(CN)]-$

The nitrile composition is about 40% by weight and the elastomer is cross-linked using sulphur. Other additives include calcium stearate and zinc oxide. A small amount of clay is added to lubricate the material – normally calcium alumino-silicates.

The failed seals showed circumferential brittle cracks, a typical example being shown in Figure 4.64. Since the seals were only 1 mm in wall thickness, scanning electron microscopy was needed to examine the cracks. Figure 4.65 shows an ESEM image of a seal with two independent cracks, an upper and a lower one. The lower crack was the critical crack because it penetrated the rubber seal. The upper has not penetrated the seal, and is thus a sub-critical crack.

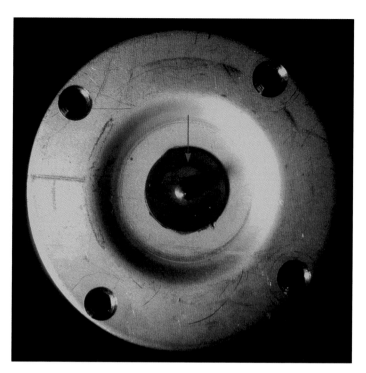

Figure 4.64   Brittle crack (marked with arrow) in rubber seal fitted to diaphragm

Figure 4.65   ESEM picture of brittle cracks in seal: the arrows indicate the two cracks

It is noticeable that the cracks have grown at the two corners of the rubber seal, and both corners are very sharp. They are, therefore, serious stress concentrators when the seal itself is stressed by the small pressure differential. Ozone attack occurred here because the critical threshold was exceeded, growth at the outer corner being faster than the inner, suggesting that the stress was greater at the outer corner than the inner.

5.2.3 Elemental analysis

The crack surfaces were amenable to X-ray analysis using environmental scanning electron microscopy (ESEM). Comparison of (a) the crack and (b) an unattacked surface gave the results shown in Figure 4.66. The elemental composition is shown by various peaks in the energy dispersive X-ray (EDX) spectrum. Carbon, hydrogen and nitrogen are present in the nitrile rubber chains at high concentrations, and so form the most intense peaks in the spectra. Sulphur is present as the cross-linking agent, together with small amounts of zinc, calcium, magnesium, silicon and aluminium. The most significant difference between the two spectra is the changed oxygen concentration.

The action of ozone as described by the earlier chain scission equation shows that the oxygen levels should be higher in the crack surface compared with an unattacked surface. However, it is important to have a standard against which to compare the two peak values. This standard could be any of the constant elements, C, N or H, but a minor element, sulphur, is a more reliable standard for accurate comparison. Using the count values given on the graphs, the ratios are as follows:

Unattacked surface: O/S = 1.5
Cracked surface: O/S = 2.9

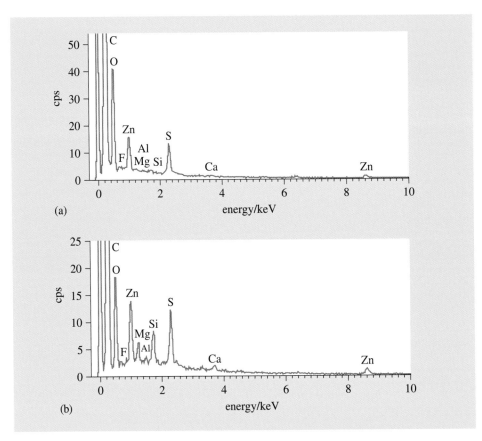

(a)

(b)

Figure 4.66   (a) Elemental analysis of crack surface; (b) elemental analysis of intact rubber surface (notice that the vertical axes of the two graphs are at different scales)

So the oxygen-to-sulphur ratio has nearly doubled on the crack surface compared with the unaffected surface, corroborating the diagnosis of ozone corrosion cracking.

By this time, direct chemical analyses were being conducted at many points in the air lines of the fabrication machines affected. They confirmed the intermittent presence of ozone and nitric oxide (another gas formed by electrical discharge). Ozone cracking is a cumulative process because once a brittle crack has been formed, there is no way it will heal or somehow disappear if the ozone disappears.

5.2.4 Ozone sources

There was a mystery over the source of the ozone in the pneumatic system. There were many filters in the air supply designed to catch any traces of compressor oil that might be carried over from the air pump and into the line. They were positioned directly behind the pump and were made of a PTFE-based microporous fabric. There were other filters closer in line to the seals, but the only ones that could absorb ozone coming from the pumps to the seals were not directly in line. Cracking of other rubber parts such as O-ring seals on chambers was also taking place, indicating a general contamination problem with the air supply.

All possible sources of ozone were examined in a detailed study of the problem, including:

- external sources such as atmospheric pollution

- external local sources such as electrical equipment nearby

- internal sources associated with the air pump.

The first two possibilities were eliminated by sampling and chemical analysis of the air intake to the pump. The final source was the compressor itself. It was a new design that did not involve oil, but instead was a dry device using contra-rotating plastic screws with a small nip at the highest compression zone. Static electricity here could cause intermittent leakage of charge, and hence formation of ozone. When all the other possibilities are eliminated then whatever is left, however improbable, must be the cause of the problem.

Eliminating the problem was reasonably low-cost, and involved:

- insertion of more filters in the line to absorb any traces of ozone

- changing the design of the seals.

The new seals were made from an ozone-resistant elastomer such as Viton, a fluorinated rubber, or EPDM, which is made from an ethylene–propylene copolymer. Neither of these has double bonds in the chain, so ozone attack is greatly inhibited. The sharp internal corner was rounded out by simply smoothing the edge of the steel tool used to compression mould the seals.

SAQ 4.16 (Learning outcomes 4.11 and 4.13)

Describe the problems created by ozone attack on elastomeric products that are critical to product and process integrity. Discuss an example of such a problem, pointing out the evidence that allowed a diagnosis of ozone stress corrosion cracking to be made. How was the problem solved?

5.3 Plumbing products

Leakage of fluid is always a very clear indicator of a failed component, and can cause great damage to property if undetected – for example, when a radiator leaks at the top of a tall building during a holiday or weekend and floods down through successive floors. With so much electronic equipment present in offices, damage can be extensive and very expensive to put right.

Much of the tubing in central heating systems is made from pure copper. This must be insulated where it meets steel radiators to prevent galvanic corrosion. However, the insulating washer must also be resistant to the high temperatures developed in radiators.

Copper is an increasingly expensive raw material, and so thermoplastics have been developed for both cold water and some hot water systems. Plastic fittings are also common because the complex shapes needed are easily reproduced in thermoplastic polymers. However, many such polymers are sensitive to chlorine, which is present in most drinking water supplies (as well as in swimming pools, as discussed earlier). They are also used less frequently in hot water systems, since few thermoplastics are heat-resistant.

5.3.1 Fitting failure

One example of a fitting failure occurred during a weekend in the Physics Department at Loughborough University. An acetal resin fitting in the plumbing system fractured unexpectedly, flooding the computer labs immediately below the sink involved. Damage was high because the leak was undetected until the Monday morning. The configuration of the plumbing below the sink is shown in Figure 4.67. The failed fitting was located at the junction between the incoming cold water supply and a heater, which supplied hot water to the sink above. This junction is shown in greater detail in Figure 4.68(a), while Figure 4.68(b) shows a close-up of the failed fitting.

EXERCISE 4.9

The first investigation suggested that the break in the lower plastic fitting had been caused by faulty fitting of the heater unit attached to the adjacent wall under the sink. The screw had become loose, allowing the considerable weight of the heater to be placed on the screw fitting of the failed joint. By considering the load path between the two components, suggest whether or not the theory can be justified.

An alternative explanation to that given in Exercise 4.9 was sought. The investigator next suggested that the screw joint had been too tightly fitted or, alternatively, that it was fitted too loosely – these are, of course, mutually exclusive options. If the screw joint was too tightly fitted, then the high tightening stresses would put high stresses at the base of the screw thread and hence promote failure. The hypothesis was not corroborated by examination of the washer, the impression on the surface being slight. The critical evidence was the fracture surface of the fitting. Could it yield the root cause of the problem?

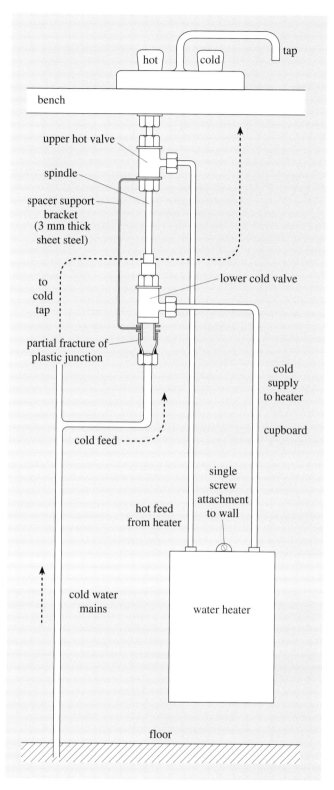

Figure 4.67   Plumbing system for tap water supply

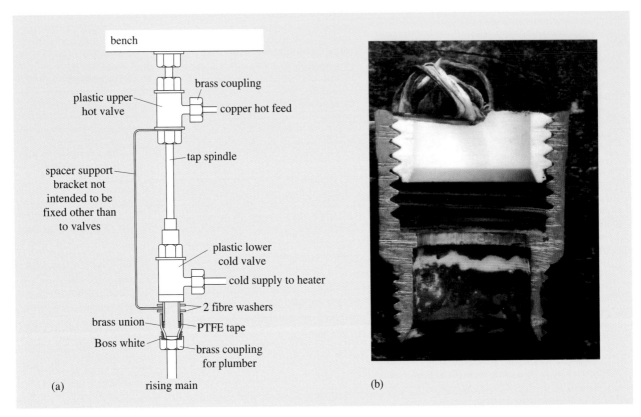

(a)

(b)

Figure 4.68   (a) Detail of hot-water mixer; (b) close-up of the failed fitting (sectioned after the failure)

5.3.2 Fracture surface

The surface seen in Figure 4.69 shows several significant features, including:

- brown contamination over most of the fracture

- a very fresh fracture surface

- the screw thread present on the exterior of the sample.

The fresh areas of the break could be explained immediately, because the first investigator reported that the sample had broken into two parts when it fell from his desk during his examination! The contamination seems to indicate that the original failure

Figure 4.69   Fracture surface of acetal resin fitting

Figure 4.70   Close-up of fracture surface showing deposit

was old, a view confirmed by the size of the deposit shown on the fracture surface of the corresponding part (Figure 4.70). The brown deposit is rather thick and covers an extensive part of the failed surface. It looks like rust, but the deposit in the electric kettle of a nearby common room was very similar, so it was probably from the water supply. It is likely to consist of salts in solution in the local water supply (probably a mixture of iron and calcium carbonates), and was probably created by slow evaporation of water leaking very slowly from a hairline fracture over a long period of time.

The results of initial examination are shown by the fracture surface map (Figure 4.71). The zones of different colouration are suggestive of multiple crack initiation, the deeper tones corresponding to parts where the cracks were widest, and therefore more deposit was formed.

Figure 4.71   Fracture surface map of the surface shown in Figure 4.69

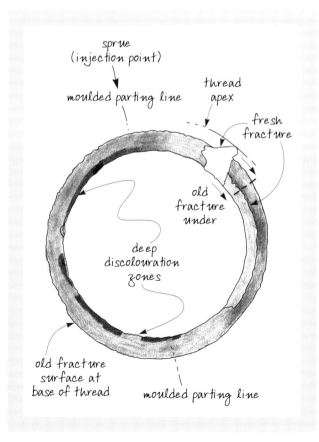

5.3.3 Microscopic inspection

The next step was to examine the fracture using a high-powered optical microscope. Figure 4.72 was taken in the screw thread, so shows the exterior of the failed fitting. The inspection revealed small defects ahead of the crack tip, as indicated by the arrows. They are aligned at an angle to the thread root, implying that they are related to the way the device has been made. Close examination of the fracture surface showed flaps of material still in site at the edges of the fracture; the orientation of these indicated the direction of travel of the several cracks involved in the failure. The results are summarized in Figure 4.73, which shows a detail of the fracture map.

Scanning microscopy was used to confirm the presence of defects, and also showed the presence of anomalous amounts of chlorine on the tiny cracks. This was an unusual discovery because chlorine is not present in the original polymer.

5.3.4 Injection moulding of plumbing system fittings

It was found that the fittings had been injection moulded in a six-cavity tool. New and unused fittings were obtained for comparison with the failed fitting. None could be matched exactly with the failed fitting, because as the material flows into the cavity it leaves so-called *flow lines* on the exterior surfaces, each particular pattern being characteristic of a particular cavity. The failed fitting showed a high level of flow lines, as well as far more serious defects known as *weld lines*. These occur where the different regions of the flowing polymer have failed to fuse in the tool, and are effectively small cracks in the outer surface of the samples affected. Weld lines that occur in zones likely to be highly stressed in service will act as stress concentrators, multiplying the net imposed stress.

However, the combined effect was probably not enough to cause critical cracking, because the material used is normally very tough and crack-resistant. Something else was needed to initiate brittle cracks in the polymer.

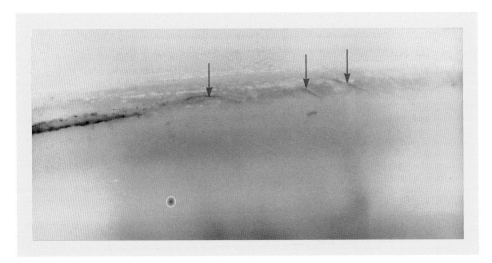

Figure 4.72   Close-up of brittle cracks ahead of crack tip (the cracks are indicated by arrows)

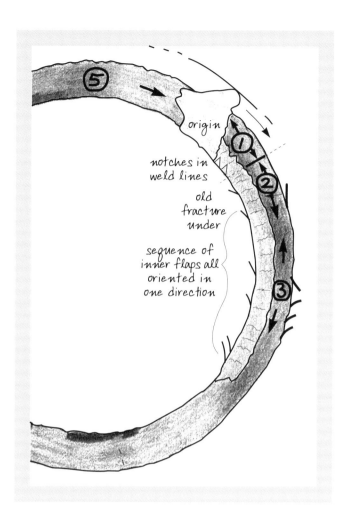

Figure 4.73 Detail of fracture map showing multiple cracks

5.3.5 Chlorine stress corrosion cracking

The mechanism that started the brittle cracks was discovered when a second investigator performed a wide literature search encompassing commercial literature (not just the academic press). An item in a technical magazine for the chemical industry published in the USA mentioned a court case then being decided in Texas.

A large number of homeowners had just been awarded substantial damages against the manufacturers of plastic piping systems, including Shell, Hoechst and DuPont, and the suppliers, US Brass Inc. The latter had supplied pipes and fittings for central heating systems, made from polybutylene (the pipe) and acetal resin (the fittings). Both types of polymer had been degraded by traces of chlorine in the water supply, probably aided by the high temperatures of hot water systems and by dissolved oxygen. The failures occurred by initiation and growth of brittle cracks in the bore of such systems, until penetration of the wall or fitting had occurred, producing catastrophic leaks and subsequent damage to the houses concerned.

The news from the USA transformed the UK case. In the first place, a check with the local water board in Loughborough revealed that significant levels of chlorine were added to the water supply for its anti-bacterial action. The levels fluctuated over time, but were especially high when pipes were being modified in roadworks, for example.

Experiments in the US case established that very low levels of free chlorine in water (5 parts per billion) could initiate stress corrosion cracks at existing defects and stress concentrations, so it was likely that the Loughborough fitting had degraded in a similar way.

Chlorine acts as an extremely powerful oxidizing agent by reacting directly with hydrogen atoms in repeat units along the polymer chain:

$$Cl_2 + -[CH_2-CH_2-O-CH_2-CH_2-O]- \rightarrow - CH_2-CHO + HCl + CHCl-CH_2-O-$$

Thus a single molecule of chlorine (Cl_2) produces a break in the chain. Since this occurs typically in a crevice or corner, the acid produced raises the pH locally, allowing hydrolysis to occur:

$$-[CH_2-CH_2-O-CH_2-CH_2-O]- + HCl \rightarrow -CH_2-CH_2OH + CHCl-CH_2-CH_2-O-$$

So the consumption of just one molecule of chlorine causes two chain breaks. This sequence of reactions explains why chlorine can have such a devastating effect on the strength of acetal polymer.

> The chemical formulae here are shown just for illustration – you don't have to remember them.

5.3.6 Failure sequence

Initiation of brittle cracks came from the small weld lines present in the sample, which should never have been approved for use by the moulders. When chlorinated tap water rose into the joint, brittle cracks formed at the welds and grew to penetrate the wall, allowing slow leakage of water from the joint. The driving force for brittle crack growth came from the closure stress imposed when the joint was screwed home, together with any residual strain present in the moulding. Because the leak was slow, water evaporated at the cracks, forming a deposit that tended to fill the cracks and slow the leak down. However, the deposit was brittle, as can be judged by the sharp edges of the contamination seen in Figure 4.70. At some time over a weekend, the joint finally burst catastrophically. The reason for the final failure will probably never be known for certain, but stress can arise through a phenomenon known as 'water hammer'. This occurs when a valve is suddenly closed somewhere in the water supply, perhaps elsewhere in the building (work was being done over the weekend on the water system). A pressure wave propagates through the water, and this was probably enough to trigger final failure of the joint (Figure 4.74).

The case highlighted the importance of quality control in manufacture, where it is vital to prevent faulty products being supplied for use. In the USA, cases still continue because of the widespread use of plastic plumbing materials in hot water systems. Although the materials are no longer used in new builds, the effects of the problem made companies much more aware of their responsibilities when introducing new materials, and the importance of testing them under realistic conditions.

SAQ 4.17 (Learning outcomes 4.11 and 4.13)

Discuss how chlorine in solution attacks polymers in a form of stress corrosion cracking (SCC). Briefly describe a case involving the failure of a plumbing fitting, explaining why the device failed through stress corrosion cracking.

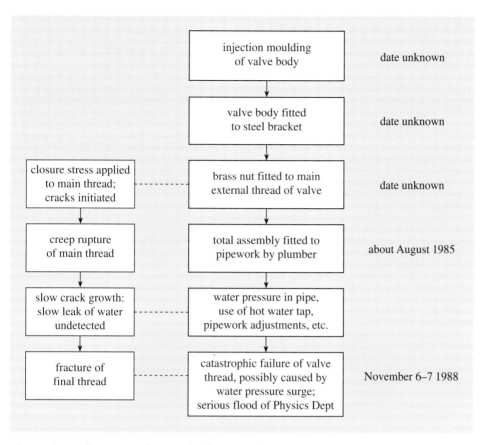

Figure 4.74   Sequence of events leading up to flood

5.4 Seal failures

Other failures have occurred in plumbing systems where the design itself is flawed in some way. Such failures are potentially more serious because many systems are affected, so the damage is not isolated to just one location.

Just this happened to many central heating systems in public buildings in the late 1990s. A number of new central heating systems had been fitted in old people's homes in the Midlands, and several schools, including a famous private school in the south-west, Benenden. To prevent galvanic corrosion occurring between copper pipes and steel radiators, non-metal washers were used on the screw joints to isolate the two metals. These washers are also used on other screwed joints, such as hot water taps and access vents in radiators, to provide a secure and leak-free joint. Such vents are needed to allow the central heating system to be bled of the hydrogen gas that builds up in the hot water system as a result of the inevitable internal corrosion of the steel that occurs over a period of time. The gas accumulates in pockets at the top of the radiator and, being an insulator, stops that part of the radiator from heating up and performing its intended function. The problem is solved simply by unscrewing the joint and releasing the pressurized gas, which vents freely into the atmosphere.

However, a few months after installation, slow leaks were discovered at numerous separate locations, leaks that had allowed significant volumes of water to escape and damage furnishings below the radiators. It was found that the polymeric seals had failed.

5.4.1 Examination of failed seals

Examination of the failed joints showed that the polymeric seals had cracked in a brittle way. This was unusual behaviour, because the polymer used was a type of synthetic rubber, which had been newly introduced by the manufacturer of the plumbing systems. Rubber washers should be capable of withstanding large closure stresses without any kind of failure, and certainly not by brittle cracking.

Two screw bleed vents are shown in Figure 4.75. These were taken from a radiator at an old people's home in Warwickshire. The brittle cracks that created the leaks can be seen at the top of the picture.

Another failed seal, taken from Benenden school, is shown in Figure 4.76 and provides further evidence of the type of failure. Here damage is more serious, there being three brittle cracks that have grown across the diameter of the seal. The arrows

Figure 4.75   Fractured radiator seals from old people's home: the two arrows indicate the location of the brittle cracks

Figure 4.76   Fractured radiator seal from Benenden school, showing seal extrusion

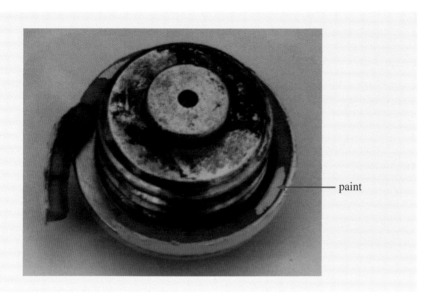

Figure 4.77   Paint on inner lip of seal

point to a permanent set in the material where a small blip has been formed by extrusion, an effect that should not occur in an elastomer. Cross-linked rubber should always return to its original shape when the stress is released (like a rubber band), a characteristic of long-range rubber elasticity.

Other seals showed traces of paint between the washer and the adjacent metal surface (Figure 4.77). There were also traces of black iron oxide, formed normally in central heating systems, on the internal metal parts of the screw fitting.

EXERCISE 4.10

What does the presence of paint on a sealing surface suggest about the effectiveness of the washer?

So the material, far from sealing the joint, had failed in its primary purpose. Controlled experiments with new seals showed that when compressed under heat they hardened rapidly with time, losing sealing capability. As they hardened, brittle cracks were initiated on the surfaces and grew across the diameter. From their appearance, it was clear that the cracks were initiated on the outer surface and grew inwards.

SAQ 4.18 (Learning outcome 4.10)

Some of the fracture surfaces in the original failed seals showed signs of striations (Figure 4.78). Suggest how such features could have been formed on the washers by considering the loads within a washer. Include a discussion of thermal problems in your answer.

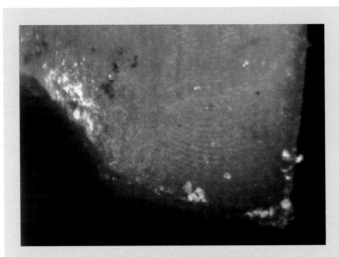

Figure 4.78   Fatigue striations on fracture surface

5.4.2 Material characteristics

It was clear from a wide range of similar failures that the material itself was unsuitable for use in this particular application. But what was the material? It was a new type of rubber known as a *thermoplastic elastomer*, or TPE for short. Such ☑ **elastomers** ☑ had been developed in the USA in the 1970s by DuPont, one of the largest US companies making a wide range of synthetic polymers. The same company originally developed nylon in the 1930s, as well as Neoprene®, a new synthetic rubber resistant to many chemicals, and widely used in demanding applications such as bridge bearings. The rubber must be cross-linked for demanding and high-stress applications, using sulphur-based reagents.

☑ Elastomers

One class of polymers offers a set of unique properties that are well exploited in most engineering structures. They are rubbers, or elastomers, solid materials that can be stretched to many times their length, yet return to their original size when the load is released. This means that they can be made into devices that absorb energy and so help to moderate unwanted vibrations from engines or other sources, since vibrations can damage structures through fatigue, for example. So what is it about their structure that confers such useful properties?

All polymers become elastomeric above a certain temperature, but only certain members have been developed commercially as rubbers. One class of

elastomers contain double bonds in the main chain. The double bonds enable the chains to rotate about their axes very easily, a requirement for good elastomeric behaviour. The best-known members are:

- natural rubber, NR (also known as polyisoprene), or $[-CH=C(CH_3)-CH_2-]_n$

- polybutadiene, PB, or $[-CH_2-CH=CH-CH_2-]_n$

- polychloroprene, PI (also known as Neoprene), or $[-CH_2-CH=CCl-CH_2-]_n$

- various copolymers of these basic structures, such as SBR rubber, a random copolymer of PB and polystyrene (PS). ▷

To minimize creep, elastomers must be cross-linked chemically to bind the chains together. Combination with sulphur (about 1%) is usually sufficient. In addition, very finely divided carbon black is added to increase the modulus of the material, making it capable of resisting high loads. The modulus of unfilled cross-linked rubber is typically only about 2 MPa, and is increased a hundredfold with about 1% carbon black added. Blends of different rubbers are used most commonly in tyre construction (Figure 4.79).

The tread is usually made from a blend of NR and SBR, a mix that has high hysteresis and absorbs a high fraction of vibrations. This means that the coefficient of friction with the road is high, for good road-holding. The sidewall is a blend of NR and PB, with low hysteresis, to minimize heat build-up when driving. Excessive heat will degrade the material, leading to failure. The structure is lined internally with butyl rubber, which has a high resistance to gas diffusion. A key component is the breaker, a stiff layer under the tread, that lengthens tyre life and improves traction. Such radial tyres commonly have steel or aramid breakers. Aramids such as Kevlar® are a type of nylon. The material is not only very stiff (tensile modulus 124 GPa, strength 2800 MPa) but also thermally very stable (to above 400 °C). The fibre is thus used in composites to increase modulus and strength, and in textile form for fireproof and bullet-proof apparel.

However, making vulcanized rubber products can be wasteful, because scrap cannot be recycled easily, and cross-linking limits the range of properties of the final product. Another type of material solves these problems: thermoplastic elastomers or TPEs. They are cross-linked by crystallites or domains, so can be recycled above the crystal melting point. They also give a much wider range of moduli and strengths, and are widely used in medical products such as catheters and niche products such as drive belts for snowmobiles.

Figure 4.79   Tyre construction

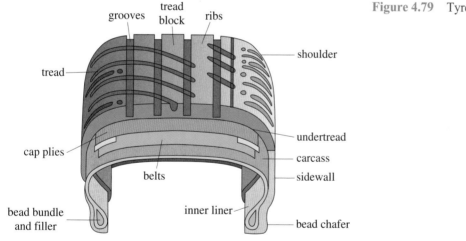

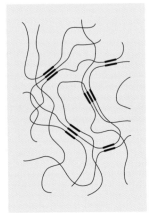

Figure 4.80 Schematic of the molecular structure of TPE

There are limits to the uses of vulcanized rubber, however. The stiffness and strength of cross-linked rubbers are limited, despite the extensive use of carbon black as a reinforcing filler. As chemical cross-linking locks the polymer chains into permanent bonds with other chains, scrap inevitably produced during manufacture cannot be recycled easily.

TPEs were developed to fill the property gaps. They are elastomers that are physically cross-linked through a second phase present in the polymer matrix (Figure 4.80). The washers were made of a block copolymer of polyester and a short chain glycol (known as Hytrel®), the polyester being shown as thick lines because these chains co-crystallize to form the second phase in the material, holding the flexible polyether chains together. Another example of failure of a TPE is given in ☑ **Catheter fracture** ☑.

☑ Catheter fracture

Catheters are used widely in medical practice for infusing drugs and other medicaments to patients. If failure occurs, the consequences are usually serious. Fracture can allow air to enter the bloodstream, for example, which could cause death if an air bubble were to travel to the brain.

During childbirth, epidural drugs can be administered to the patient via the spinal fluid. This anaesthetizes the lower half of her body, so relieving labour pains.

Many different polymers can and have been used for such tubes, TPEs offering one choice for their flexibility and strength. A typical epidural catheter is a tube of 1 mm diameter, closed at one end, into which three holes are formed for the drug liquid to escape into the spinal fluid. However, one such catheter fractured at one of the holes during an operation (Figure 4.81), leaving a small piece of plastic in the patient. She sued the hospital, the anaesthetist and the

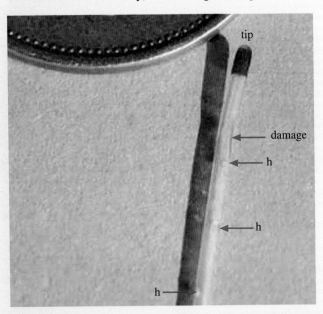

Figure 4.81 Epidural catheter: the tip, the damage zone and the three holes (h) are marked

manufacturer of the device, and thus it was necessary to determine the cause of the failure.

One expert alleged that the doctor had wrongly withdrawn the tube, cutting it axially with the sharp edge of the hollow needle used to hold it in place. However, the failed surface told a different story (Figures 4.82 and 4.83).

The surface showed a mainly brittle fracture with no trace of blade marks, and only limited ductility. The material, a TPE of nylon and polyether, should normally be completely ductile. The fracture had occurred at a stress concentration – one of the holes formed in the side of the catheter – so it was inferred that mild usage loads had caused the failure.

But what had embrittled the material? The nurses at the time of the operation had reported that the end of the catheter remote from the patient had shattered and been mended with tape, so it was likely that the polymer had been embrittled by some environmental agent. Chemical analysis suggested that the polymer

Figure 4.82 Failure surface of catheter

had been degraded by ultraviolet (UV) radiation, a well-known cause of premature failure in many polymers. They are usually protected against UV attack by special additives, but these cannot be used in medical-grade polymers for fear of them leaching into the body. The doctor and hospital involved were exonerated, and the manufacturer paid substantial damages to the injured woman.

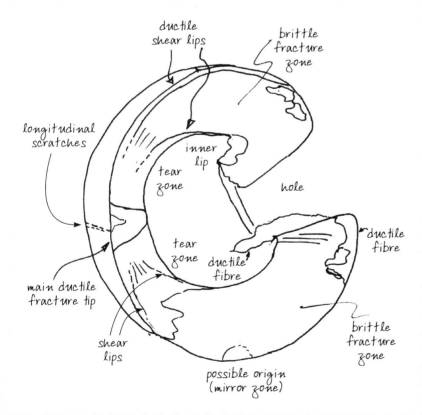

Figure 4.83 Fracture map of the surface shown in Figure 4.82

5.4.3 Failure mechanisms

One possible reason for the failure of the Hytrel washers is that the polyether chains in Hytrel can be hydrolysed by water at high temperatures. This has several knock-on effects. The first is a loss of chain molecular weight and a consequent lowering of strength. The second problem occurs because the free polyester segments crystallize and stiffen the material. This causes shrinkage and permanent set of the material, with loss of long-range elasticity.

The loss of strength of Hytrel has been well studied, and is summarized in Figure 4.84. The tensile strength is described in terms of the tensile *half-life*, the time it takes for the strength to halve in value. The value decreases with the reciprocal of temperature. So exposure of the material to water of temperature 50 °C will lead to loss of half its strength in about 100 days, while exposure at 70 °C causes the half-life to fall to only 40 days. The process can be slowed by adding 10% of an inhibitor (MS), as demonstrated by Figure 4.84. However, the material remains sensitive to hydrolysis and loss of strength with exposure to high temperatures.

It transpired that the manufacturer had used Hytrel washers successfully in cold and hot water taps without any signs of failure. There the material was exposed only infrequently and intermittently to high temperatures, so its life before failure would have been long. It was subsequently assumed that Hytrel could be used in a quite different environment involving continuous or frequent exposure to high temperatures, which was quite wrong, as this case study has shown.

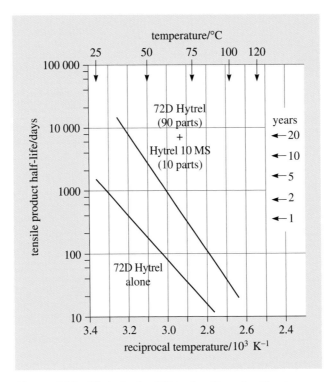

Figure 4.84   Hydrolysis of Hytrel, with and without an added inhibitor

SAQ 4.19 (Learning outcome 4.16)

It is proposed to use Hytrel for an external rotor shaft seal on a small outboard motor fitted to a small boat. What lifetime would you expect for application in a vessel used in:

(a) temperate water (mean $t_c \approx 21$ °C)

(b) tropical water (mean $t_c \approx 30$ °C)?

Give the lifetimes for both unprotected Hytrel and Hytrel protected with 10 parts of MS.

Which grade of Hytrel would you recommend for this application? What practical considerations should be taken into account in order to provide a better estimate of lifetime?

SAQ 4.20 (Learning outcomes 4.11 and 4.13)

Describe the problem of hydrolysis in terms of the results of inappropriate use of a thermoplastic elastomer (Hytrel TPE) in a central heating system. What effects does hydrolysis have on the mechanical properties? Indicate what tests should have been conducted on the product before it was used in service.

5.4.4 Aftermath

The results of the failure of the seal led to several claims for damages from the manufacturer, who should have tested the material in realistic conditions before launching the seals into circulation.

6 SUMMARY

As demonstrated in the case studies in this block, initial design of a new product must attempt to take into account all possible factors that may affect its lifetime, especially if a long service life is contemplated. That means designing the structure or product with a high safety factor, especially if it is to be exposed to harsh climatic conditions or severe usage. Product under-design pares the safety factor to the very limits and will lead to the kind of failures discussed in this block. Designers need to account fully for the environment that a product will be exposed to, as well as the stresses it must bear.

LEARNING OUTCOMES

After studying this part you should be able to do the following:

4.1 Differentiate between and describe dissolution, degradation and corrosion as they affect the deterioration of structural materials.

4.2 Describe in simple terms the chemical reactions involved in deterioration.

4.3 Use simple models to calculate the stresses induced in physical processes.

4.4 Predict electrochemical behaviour between dissimilar metals.

4.5 Explain galvanic corrosion in terms of the electrochemical series.

4.6 Distinguish between the hoop and longitudinal stresses in a pressure-vessel wall, and specify them in terms of the pressure, wall thickness and diameter of the vessel.

4.7 Describe the loads in the various parts of a structure and the most likely load path.

4.8 Indicate the procedures needed in practical failure analysis.

4.9 Specify the failure mechanisms possible when a nominally ductile material fails in a brittle fashion.

4.10 Relate crack formation to the loads on a component, bearing in mind the importance of stress concentrations in the component concerned.

4.11 Provide a likely sequence of events involved in the failure of a part made from several different components.

4.12 Describe the problem of fretting wear at a bearing joint.

4.13 Describe the key circumstances of a particular accident or disaster, and relate the sequence of events to specific causes supported by the relevant evidence.

4.14 Calculate the thermal expansion of products given necessary data.

4.15 Estimate the amount of corrosion product formed using relevant data.

4.16 Estimate the rate of degradation from data provided.

ANSWERS TO EXERCISES

EXERCISE 4.1

(a) Rusting is a form of corrosion where the iron of the roof is converted to iron oxide, or red-brown rust.

(b) Removal of limestone by rain water is a kind of dissolution process, where the calcium carbonate goes into solution.

(c) Rot is a form of degradation of the cellulose fibres in wood by natural organisms like fungi (such as dry or wet rot).

EXERCISE 4.2

The hoop stress is given by:

$$\sigma_h = \frac{pr}{t_c}$$

where p is the internal pressure, r the radius of the cylinder and t_c the wall thickness. The hoop stress acts such that the pipe will fail by a lengthways crack.

With the data provided, assuming no wall thinning, then:

$$\sigma_h = \frac{pr}{t_c} = \frac{4.65 \times 10^6 \text{ Pa} \times 380 \times 10^{-3} \text{ m}}{7.6 \times 10^{-3} \text{ m}} = 232 \text{ MPa}$$

With wall thinning to 2.5 mm due to the effects of corrosion, however, at failure:

$$\sigma_h = \frac{pr}{t_c} = \frac{4.65 \times 10^6 \text{ Pa} \times 380 \times 10^{-3} \text{ m}}{2.5 \times 10^{-3} \text{ m}} = 700 \text{ MPa}$$

EXERCISE 4.3

The Statue had corroded seriously in 100 years while HMS *Alarm* had corroded in only 2 years. The ship was subjected to continuous immersion in sea water, a good conductor owing to its high salt content, while the statue was subjected to only intermittent rain-water percolation through leaks in the outer copper skin. On the *Alarm*, the iron nails had a very small area, which meant that they corroded very quickly.

EXERCISE 4.4

Reading from Table 4.2, the separation of steel and bronze is greater than that of steel and magnesium, so one might suggest that corrosion would be greatest for the steel/bronze couple.

However, looking at electrode potentials (Table 4.1), the standard E^0 values are:

> Mg/Mg^{2+}: $E^0 = -2.37$ V
>
> Fe/Fe^{2+}: $E^0 = -0.44$ V
>
> Cu/Cu^{2+}: $E^0 = +0.34$ V

The difference between magnesium and iron is much larger than that between iron and copper, so the electrochemical series contradicts the galvanic series in this case. The electrochemical series is a more accurate predictor of corrosion behaviour than the galvanic series alone.

EXERCISE 4.5

The root of the thread of any screwed joint represents a stress concentrator, where the applied stress can be magnified many times at the corner. The exact value of K_t will depend on the radius of curvature at the root, sharper roots being more severe than shallow roots.

EXERCISE 4.6

It is always best if a corresponding part to a fracture surface is examined, because it can corroborate features present on the half of the surface already found. It is especially important where subsequent damage such as corrosion has occurred. If eye bar 330 had fractured at an early stage in the disaster, it would be vital to determine the cause of the brittle fracture.

EXERCISE 4.7

The shank dimensions are 51 mm by 305 mm, giving a section area of 15.6×10^{-3} m^2, while the limbs at each side of the hole are each 203 by 51 mm, giving a total section of 20.7×10^{-3} m^2. So the section area is about a third greater in the limb compared with the shank, giving a correspondingly lower stress.

Nevertheless, the greater stress concentration at the edges of the hole should have ensured failure here rather than in the shank.

Surface roughness effects can be critical, so if the pin and eye-bar hole surfaces were smooth and the shank surface was rough, failure in the shank would be preferred.

EXERCISE 4.8

Cut-outs in an aircraft fuselage will raise the local stress to high levels. Square windows, for example, have four sharp corners that will act as stress concentrators.

EXERCISE 4.9

The weight of the heater unit is supported by the two vertical connecting pipes if the screw fixing to the wall has come free. They will be in tension and the total weight transferred to the top joint above the mixing unit. However, it is supported from below by the cold water mains pipe, so the total load on the top joint will be lower than the total mass of the heater unit. The longer pipe may be put into bending by a skew load, and then supported by the steel bracket holding the water mixing unit together. It is thus very unlikely that the loose screw could put any load on the lower plastic fitting.

EXERCISE 4.10

Either the joint had not been tightened up sufficiently when fitted or the washer had shrunk. The former is unlikely because leakage would probably have occurred before the radiator was painted. This implies that the washer had changed its dimensions, and shrunk away from the sealing surface for paint to bleed into the gap.

ANSWERS TO SELF-ASSESSMENT QUESTIONS

SAQ 4.1

(a) Tin ($E^0 = -0.14$ V) is less reactive, with a less negative electrode potential, than iron ($E^0 = -0.44$ V, Table 4.1). Iron will thus be attacked preferentially in the galvanic cells set up where the tin layer is broken. The rate of rusting will be rapid owing to the galvanic action set up between the two metals, especially in an external environment with exposure to slightly acidic rain.

(b) Zinc ($E^0 = -0.76$ V) lies below iron ($E^0 = -0.44$ V) with a more negative potential in the electrochemical series, so will corrode instead of the iron, which remains structurally intact until the zinc is consumed. After that, the iron will rust away until destroyed.

SAQ 4.2

There are two stress components in the wall of a cylindrical boiler, the hoop stress and the longitudinal stress. The hoop stress is twice the longitudinal stress and is given by the equation:

$$\sigma_h = \frac{pr}{t_c}$$

where p is the internal pressure, r the radius of the cylinder and t the wall thickness. The hoop stress acts such that the cylinder will fail by a lengthways crack (rather than a radial crack).

A riveted joint will always be weaker than continuous material, simply because it is a break in the uniformity of the wall. The rivet holes themselves are stress concentrators, and a line of rivets is a line of such defects, so the line of rivets is the weakest part of the structure.

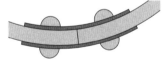

The problem could be tackled by replacing the lap joint with a butt joint (Figure 4.85), reinforced by extra layers of riveted metal.

Figure 4.85 Reinforced butt joint

SAQ 4.3

(a) The towers support all the suspension chains, the hangers and the trussed roadway. This load puts the tower structure into compression.

(b) The roadway is supporting its self-weight and any traffic, and it will be in bending.

(c) Each eye bar is under tension, supporting the tension in the main chain at either side, and the downward-pointing tension from the hanger.

(d) The pin is in a state of bending from the successive tension loads from the separate bars in the joint.

The top eye-bar joints should be under greatest tensile load because they support the complete length of chain below. The load diminishes at successively lower eye-bar joints.

SAQ 4.4

There are several possible mechanisms that can cause brittle behaviour in any nominally ductile material such as steel:

- excessively low temperatures, below the steel's ductile-to-brittle transition temperature
- severe stress concentrations
- pre-existing cracks
- fatigue cracking
- stress corrosion cracking (SCC)
- any combination of these mechanisms.

SAQ 4.5

(a) The joint consists of four eye bars fitted onto a steel pin, with covers bolted on either side to prevent the outer bars falling off. There is a set of two inner bars and a set of two outer bars. At eye-bar joint 330, the north-facing outer bar cracked in a brittle fashion at the lower part of the eye, from a defect present on the inside surface of the eye itself. Both of the upper bars will have been slightly more heavily loaded than the two lower eye bars because they will have borne the combined tension of the lower chain and the weight of the deck transmitted from the hanger. The load path leads from the hanger to the centre pin holding the joint together, to the bearing surfaces of the upper eye bars.

(b) The bearing surfaces will be on the inside surface of the eye, one at the shank side and one 180° away on the inner surface. Because there was a clearance of about 3 mm between the pin and the eye, there will have been a gap along the lower edge of the fit of a maximum of 3 mm. The maximum tensile load will therefore have been at two points opposite one another, and at roughly 90° to the bearing points. They are at the lowest and highest parts of the inner surface of the eye. The maximum tensile load will have been about three times the nominal applied load owing to the stress-concentrating effects of a hole, the eye of the bar.

(c) The gap between the pin and eye will be exposed to the environment, and will tend to fill with rain water. Rusting will tend to occur there, and if there are any pre-existing cracks, crevice corrosion will develop. Red-brown rust will be formed first, followed by black oxide where the oxygen gradient is low, i.e. at the deepest parts of the crack or cracks.

SAQ 4.6

Fretting wear occurs owing to repeated cyclical movement at a joint and was caused in the Silver Bridge pin joints by corrosion producing particles of $Fe_2O_3.2H_2O$ that were harder than the underlying steel, and of greater volume. The action will have been most severe at the upper joints on the main chains, where the loads were largest. Tension cracks through fatigue could have formed at either side of the contact zone between the edge of the eye bar and the central pin. Although fretting fatigue had been shown in the tests to be a possible failure mode, the mechanism demands that fatigue cracks could grow only very near the points of contact between the eye-bar hole and the pin. Since the main load will occur along the chain, the contact zones will be on the long axis and not at 90° to the axis. The critical crack was found on the lower edge of the pin-hole at 90° to the axis, so is unlikely to have been formed by fretting fatigue.

SAQ 4.7

(a) Stress corrosion cracking was known to occur in high-pressure boilers: many examples had occurred on the railways from the 1840s onwards, especially in Britain, but also elsewhere as the railway networks expanded worldwide. The first study of the problem showed that boiler walls tended to crack at grooves or corners in the shell, often from the overlapping longitudinal joint in the boiler. The inner corner represented not only a serious stress concentrator but also a zone where liquid water collected, encouraging rusting. With daily pressurization, crack growth was encouraged by fatigue. The problem of groove cracking was removed only by changing the design of boilers to use a riveted butt joint, thus eliminating the corner at the heart of the problem.

The problem of SCC was also encountered in India in the 1920s, in the premature detonation of rifle shells. It was caused by attack on the copper content of the brass shell case by traces of ammonia in the air. The gas, which is produced during rotting of animal wastes, attacked cases that had been deformed during manufacture, leaving high levels of residual stress in the upper edges of the cases, where cracks were initiated. The problem was eliminated by annealing the shell cases to lower the residual stress, and storing the shells well away from sources of ammonia.

(b) The other problem in the joints was fretting corrosion caused by small rotary movements between the pin and the eye-bar inner surface. At high imposed stress at the bearing surface, Hertzian loading creates a local compressive zone surrounded by a tensile zone. Rusting produces hard particles of hydrated iron oxide of greater volume than the original iron. The particles abrade the bearing surfaces, creating surface pits and grooves that can act as nuclei for fatigue cracks. With the joints being totally exposed to the environment, rusting in the joint (followed by fretting wear) was foreseeable. The protective action of the silver paint was completely ineffective because the inner parts of the joint could not be reached by the paint. A protective bearing surface should have been incorporated onto the pin and eye-bar inner surfaces.

SAQ 4.8

The Silver Bridge accident occurred owing to stress corrosion cracking of a pin joint (no. 330) on the upper part of the subsidiary suspension chain on the north of the Ohio side of the structure. The critical crack occurred at the bottom of the north-facing lower eye bar of the joint. Each joint comprised two pairs of hardened steel eye bars fitted onto a steel pin with screwed caps to close the joint. The joint was the first one below the top of the Ohio tower. The accident happened about 39 years after construction, when the crack became sufficiently deep to grow catastrophically. The disaster happened for a combination of reasons, including the following:

1   The joints of the bridge had been painted after construction, but the paint failed to protect the inner bearing surfaces.

2   Inspection of the bridge joints could not reveal the corrosion problem caused by lack of a protective coating, since the bearing parts were totally inaccessible.

3   Fretting corrosion occurred at the joints over a long period of time, encouraging initiation of stress corrosion cracks at the most highly stressed part of the joint at right angles to the axis of the main chain. The critical crack occurred at the lower part of the joint where water would naturally tend to collect.

4   The crack was encouraged to grow by a very high level of tensile residual stress in the eye bar, itself probably caused during manufacture by casting followed by heat treatment and machining. The residual stress in the edge of the eye-bar hole was up to a third of the yield stress of the steel.

5   The fracture toughness of the eye bar was low owing to the hardening process that increased the stiffness of the material. It was further lowered by the freezing conditions on the morning of the accident.

6   Sulphur compounds were found in the corrosion cracks, suggesting that they exacerbated crack growth.

The evidence in support included direct examination of the failed eye-bar fracture and other surfaces, and tests on eye-bar steel including residual stress experiments by removal of material. X-ray analysis was used to examine the cracks in eye bar 330 for traces of impurities.

SAQ 4.9

(a) The change in length of the steel beam is:

$$\Delta L = L - L_0 = \alpha L_0 \Delta T = 11 \times 10^{-6}\ \mathrm{K}^{-1} \times 100\ \mathrm{K} \times 30.5\ \mathrm{m} = 0.034\ \mathrm{m}$$

So the beam changes in length by 34 mm.

(b) A clearance greater than 34 mm will be sufficient to allow for expansion and contraction of the beam. The equivalent change in width of the deck will be less than half this value, about 14 mm.

(c) If the beam were constrained, then a compressive stress would be formed during expansion of the deck. The strain is $0.034/30.5 = 0.11\%$, so the stress set up by expansion on the long side of the deck will be given by the product of the elastic modulus of steel and the strain:

$$\mathrm{stress} = 210 \times 10^9\ \mathrm{MPa} \times 0.11/100 = 234\ \mathrm{MPa}$$

The stress might cause distortion of the structure.

SAQ 4.10

(a) The range of loads exerted by rusting can be estimated from the range of stresses exerted by rusting within the bearing cavity, and the known area exposed to those stresses. The former were supplied by the inquiry, while the latter can be calculated from known dimensions. The inquiry estimated that the pressure varied between the limits 30 and 55 MPa. The area of the joint is simply given by using the formula πr^2, where r is the radius of the joint (Figure 4.39). The area of the pin must be subtracted to find the effective area A_f against which the rust acts. So:

$$A_f = \pi r_1^2 - \pi r_2^2 = \pi\left(178^2 - 89^2\right)\text{mm}^2 = 74\ 654\ \text{mm}^2 = 7.5\times10^{-2}\ \text{m}^2$$

We know that stress = load/area, so at the bottom of the range, the load will be:

$$\text{load in joint} = 30\times10^6\ \text{Pa}\times7.5\times10^{-2}\ \text{m}^2 = 2250\ \text{kN}$$

and at the top of the pressure range:

$$\text{load in joint} = 55\times10^6\ \text{Pa}\times7.5\times10^{-2}\ \text{m}^2 = 4125\ \text{kN}$$

Therefore the load in the joint would have varied from 2250 to 4125 kN.

(b) Rusting would have occurred by percolation of water through the edges of the joint and reaction with the unprotected steel inside. The water will have been effectively trapped within the cavity until consumed by rusting, although it would be replenished by new percolation.

(c) The pressure exerted by black oxide will be lower, since the volume expansion is lower than with brown rust. The volume expansion is approximately 50%; this is considerably less than for rusting to red-brown hydrated oxide, which has a volume expansion of over 100%.

SAQ 4.11

The Mianus River bridge was built using reinforced concrete piers supporting the road decks. They in turn comprised massive cantilevers between which were four suspended decks. The decks comprised a steel framework with a concrete road surface finished with asphalt; each deck was supported by four bearings, the outer ones (furthest from the spine of the bridge) being non-redundant. These outer hanger bearings held the suspended spans in position and allowed for expansion/contraction loads in the structure as a result of changes in ambient temperature. In 1973, the decision was taken to resurface the road and cover the drains to minimize running and maintenance costs. For the next 10 years, road water was able to pour down through the hanger bearings.

Water percolated into the bearings during this period; in winter the water contained salt added to the road for anti-icing protection. Rusting occurred within the cavity between two washers covering the central pin of each bearing. Owing to the high volume expansion of steel when it rusts, high pressures were exerted on the shaft of the pin, moving the vertical hangers off the pin. This process continued for some unknown length of time before the final failure of the bearing at the south-east corner of one of the decks at the eastern end of the bridge; all the eight bearings on the four suspended decks were later found to have deteriorated by the same process.

When the lower pin failed, the load on the upper pin was doubled, and a fatigue crack started at a sharp corner machined into the edge of the pin next to the web of the intervening support girder of the deck. The live load was a high proportion of the total load on each deck, and varied with traffic flow, being greater for loaded trucks travelling in the slow or outside lane directly above the hanger that failed.

The pin finally fractured a few hours before the final accident, allowing the deck to drop about 100 mm. Although noticed by two drivers, it went unreported until about 1.30 a.m. on 28 June 1983. At this time, three vehicles weighing nearly 700 kN were travelling in parallel lanes on the deck and it gave way, crashing to the river 21 m below. All three vehicles and a following car fell into the void; there were three fatalities and three people were severely injured.

The disaster was similar to the Silver Bridge accident of 1967, critical failure occurring at one of the joints, where steel eye bars or hangers broke, and either the whole or part of the structure collapsing. Neither type of joint was protected against rust, especially on their inner bearing surfaces, and deteriorated with time and exposure to the elements. The Silver Bridge eye bar failed due to stress corrosion cracking, while the Mianus bridge failed through widespread rusting followed by fatigue. The maintenance and inspection of both bridges had been neglected, although it is fair to say that most of the serious damage was inaccessible to direct visual inspection.

SAQ 4.12

The stresses in an aircraft fuselage are just like those in a pressure vessel. The hoop stress in a thin cylinder is given by:

$$\sigma_h = \frac{pr}{t_c}$$

where r is the radius of the cylinder and t_c the wall thickness. For an aircraft, p will be the difference between the internal and the external pressure.

The bulk of this stress will be supported by the circumferential hoops, and only a fraction transmitted to the skin. However, the transmitted hoop stress will act on the lap joint, tending to pull it apart; this will be resisted by the adhesive bond and three rows of rivets. If debonding occurs, the load will be transferred to the rivet rows alone, the upper row being most susceptible. Fatigue cracks will thus start along the axis of the row at the round edge with a nominal stress concentration factor of three (actually less owing to the lowering effect of the line of holes). Since the two sheets are no longer bonded together, and indeed forced apart by corrosion products, cracking will start at the thinnest part, that is, at the knife-edge corner.

SAQ 4.13

(a) Where debonding of the epoxy film occurred, there would be a very thin gap between the epoxy and the underlying metal. When exposed to liquid water, such gaps would fill with water by capillary action and corrosion of the metal would start to occur. Corrosion would be encouraged by any damage to the protective oxide layer.

(b) The volume of hydrated aluminium oxide ($Al_2O_3.3H_2O$) is, as one might expect, greater than the source metal. With a density of 2.42 g cm^{-3} compared with a metal density of 2.702 g cm^{-3}, the volume increase is about 10% over the metal. The increase in volume of the hydrated oxide will have encouraged further debonding by exerting a force orthogonal to the skin, tending to separate the two sheets at the overlap. Shear forces would be set up at the bonded interface by pressurization during flight cycling, further weakening the interlayer. The load-bearing capacity of the aluminium skin will have been reduced by corrosion thinning.

(c) Local factors of importance will have included the very high number of flight cycles due to the way the airline operated by flying between the islands, encouraging fatigue crack growth. The plane was flying in a marine environment; this means it is likely that it will have picked up sea spray and so the water entering the debonded zone will have been highly conductive owing to the salt content, thus encouraging corrosion. Salt solution will also have kept the capillary surfaces wetter for a longer period.

Whether or not freeze–thaw cycling could have acted in concert with corrosion is unknown, but it is another possible failure mechanism. Hawaii is a tropical archipelago, but temperature decreases rapidly with height, so the mechanism cannot be entirely excluded.

SAQ 4.14

Aloha flight 243 suffered a serious accident on 28 April 1988 when part of the forward fuselage was lost during explosive decompression. A flight attendant was lost through the hole in the fuselage, but the aircraft managed to land safely. It was an old Boeing 737 aircraft, which had been used to make short, local flights and had therefore undergone nearly 90 000 flight cycles. The fuselage in early models of the Boeing 737 was made from sheets of aluminium alloy attached to a space frame. The sheets (0.9 mm thick) were riveted together at numerous lap joints. The joint was strengthened by using an epoxy film as an adhesive to bond the sheets together, followed by three rows of rivets.

However, debonding of the epoxy resin adhesive could occur owing to poor control of manufacture. It was a cold-cure adhesive, requiring low-temperature storage before use. As it warmed for application to the metal, water condensation could occur and if left at the interface could weaken the metal–polymer bond. Premature cross-linking could also occur. Such problems led to extensive debonding of the lap joint.

The problem was well known, and had caused one disaster on a Taiwanese aircraft, which crashed with the loss of 110 people in 1981.

Debonding of the lap joint near the front of the aircraft occurred and corrosion followed as water, probably with some salt content, diffused into the thin crevice during local flights. The salt content ensured rapid corrosion to hydrated aluminium oxide with a volume expansion of about 10%. This put the joint under intense local load, acting to widen the joint further as well as thinning the skin. The final event in the sequence occurred at the inner row of rivet holes, which acted as stress concentrators for the hoop stress occurring during flights. Fatigue cracks were initiated at the edges of the holes, and grew from a knife edge on the countersunk hole. Continued pressurization cycling encouraged growth of the cracks until they reached a critical state at the time of the accident.

The cracks were spotted by one passenger at the start of the flight, but Aloha's inspection methods had clearly failed to spot the problem. This was found to be a primary cause of the accident, and several other aircraft in the same fleet were suffering the same problem of debonding, corrosion and fatigue. They were scrapped after correct inspection.

SAQ 4.15

Diesel fuel from a moving vehicle spilled onto the road and caused several following cars to skid uncontrollably on the greasy surface. The driver of one car involved in a head-on collision was seriously injured. Police tracked the fuel leak to the vehicle and found a circumferential split in the return pipe close to the engine.

The Forensic Science Service attributed the split to vandalism, but the part was buried deep in the engine compartment and was unlikely to have been attacked.

Analysis of the fracture surface showed that the break had been initiated by corrosion at the edge due to a small leak of sulphuric acid from the battery above. A connector in the pipe was made of nylon 6,6, which is highly susceptible to acid hydrolysis.

A stress corrosion crack grew intermittently across the pipe under low loads from the engine, which were most severe when the engine was started each morning. There were about 7 major striations, suggesting that the pipe had been leaking for about a week. The investigation determined that the driver should have spotted the leak and mended the pipe.

SAQ 4.16

Ozone cracking occurs when free ozone gas in the environment attacks and cleaves double bonds present in the polymer backbone. The elastomeric product must be under a degree of strain, but the strain required for crack initiation is very low, about 1% strain compared with a maximum strain of up to 800% in many rubbers.

Ozone cracking was diagnosed in a critical nitrile rubber seal used to support an air bearing in a semiconductor fabrication unit. Because it cracked, the air pressure was lost and the unit ceased to function. The diagnosis was supported by direct chemical analysis of the air in the pneumatic system, and independent EDX analysis of the crack surface (compared with an intact surface). The cause was traced to a new type of pump installed in the unit, which produced tiny amounts of ozone gas. The filters on the air supply were not sufficient to remove the gas.

The solution to the problem lay in using better-positioned filters and changing the elastomer used in the seals to an ozone-resistant rubber like EPDM with no sharp corners to act as stress concentrators.

SAQ 4.17

Chlorine dissolved in water is a very powerful oxidizing agent, which is why it is commonly added to potable drinking-water supplies to kill bacteria and viruses. It also attacks and degrades many polymers, by cleaving the chain in a reaction that produces hydrochloric acid. The strength of the polymer product drops rapidly, usually producing brittle cracks in areas that are under strain or possess high levels of residual strain.

This problem has been observed in numerous plumbing fittings in the USA, and in a case in Britain. A plumbing fitting failed over a weekend and caused much physical damage to property. Examination of the circumstances ruled out the obvious explanations, such as slippage of a heater tank on an adjacent wall, or over-tightening of the joint. Detailed microscopic inspection of the fracture surface showed that the fracture was old, and had become filled with hard water deposits from the water supply due to a very slow leak in the fitting. The sample showed multiple crack initiation and EDX analysis revealed the presence of chlorine in the fracture surfaces. The moulding itself showed several defects (flow lines) that could not be matched to good mouldings. It implied that the fitting was poorly made and possessed a high level of residual strain. Chlorine in the water supply attacked the fitting at the defects and several cracks grew as a result of SCC of the polymer. The final failure was probably caused by a surge in the water pressure.

SAQ 4.18

Fatigue occurs as a result of cyclical loads on a product, and the load can come from a variety of different sources. For example, when a constrained component is heated, it expands and the forces created by expansion are frequently sufficient to result in fatigue, especially if the material is already weak and/or brittle. The striations were probably associated with the cyclic (perhaps daily) use of the central heating system.

The seal material itself had already been weakened, as shown by the brittle cracks, and so was vulnerable to thermal fatigue.

SAQ 4.19

The applicability of the material can be assessed using the graphical data in Figure 4.84.

(a) For a Celsius temperature of 21 °C, the absolute temperature is given by:

$$T/K = t_C/°C + 273$$

So the temperature in kelvin is 294 K. The reciprocal of this temperature is:

$$1/294 \text{ K} = 3.4 \times 10^{-3} \text{ K}^{-1}$$

Extrapolating on the graph for a temperature of 294 K, the intersection with the lower curve gives:

half-life, $t_1 = 2000$ days, or 2000/365 = 5.5 years for Hytrel

and

half-life, $t_2 = 80\,000$ days, or 80 000/365 = 220 years for the protected Hytrel

(b) At the higher temperature of 30 °C (303 K), the reciprocal absolute temperature is:

$$1/303 \text{ K} = 3.3 \times 10^{-3} \text{ K}^{-1}$$

Therefore:

half-life, $t_3 = 1000$ days, or 1000/365 = 2.7 years for Hytrel

half-life, $t_4 = 20\,000$ days, or 20 000/365 = 55 years for the protected Hytrel

The protected elastomer should give higher lifetimes under both conditions. However, there are many underlying assumptions to this kind of argument that must be considered, including the variation in temperature with time and the local heating effects produced by friction of the steel shaft against the elastomer seal. It is higher temperatures that produce the damage, and the effect accelerates fast with even small rises in temperature. So the estimates will be over-optimistic predictions of half-lives compared with reality.

SAQ 4.20

Polyester–polyether elastomers are susceptible to hydrolysis or attack by water at high temperatures. The water molecules attack the ether bond and cleave the chain, so lowering the strength very rapidly.

The problem was exposed when washers were made in Hytrel elastomer for use in central heating systems. The material had previously been used successfully in cold and hot water taps, where exposure to high temperatures is infrequent and brief. The manufacturer then assumed that the same material could be used successfully in central heating systems where the washers would be exposed to high and semi-continuous temperatures.

Under these conditions, hydrolysis ensued and the chains in the polymer were broken, lowering the strength of the product. At the same time, crystallization was encouraged because the chains were smaller and thus more mobile, so the stiffness actually increased, further encouraging the initiation of brittle cracks.

The problem appeared in several guises, which might have given some warning of further and more serious problems ahead. Thus at some point the radiators were painted at one location, and paint found its way into the sealed surface. This indicated that the seal had stiffened and was no longer sealing the metal surfaces. Eventually brittle cracks were formed and these grew as thermal loads put them under extra stress. In some cases thermal fatigue occurred, judging by striations found on some fracture surfaces after the event.

The washers should have been tested under much more realistic conditions. They should have been exposed to expected central heating system temperatures under compressive load for variable times so as to assess their behaviour under conditions comparable to those found in service.

REFERENCES

Bennett, J. A. and Mindlin, H. (1973) 'Metallurgical Aspects of the Failure of the Point Pleasant Bridge', *Journal of Testing and Evaluation*, vol. 1, issue 2, pp. 152–61.

Lewis, P.R. and Hainsworth, S.V. (2006) 'Fuel line failure from stress corrosion cracking', *Engineering Failure Analysis*, vol. 13, issue 6, pp. 946–62.

Lewis, P.R., Reynolds, K. and Gagg, C. (2004) *Forensic Materials Engineering*, CRC Press.

Lichtenstein, A.G. (1993) 'The Silver Bridge Collapse Recounted', *Journal of Performance of Constructed Facilities*, vol. 7, issue 4, pp. 249–61.

Ministry of Transportation (MTO) (2003) *Sgt. Aubrey Cosens V.C. Memorial Bridge over the Montreal River at Latchford. Investigation of Failure: Final Report*, St. Catharines, Ontario, MTO.

National Transportation Safety Board (NTSB) (1971) *Collapse of U.S. 35 Highway Bridge, Point Pleasant, West Virginia, December 15, 1967* (Highway Accident Report NTSB/HAR–71/01), Washington D.C., NTSB.

National Transportation Safety Board (NTSB) (1984) *Collapse of a Suspended Span of Interstate Route 95 Highway Bridge Over the Mianus River, Greenwich, Connecticut, June 28, 1983* (Highway Accident Report NTSB/HAR–84/03), Washington D.C., NTSB.

National Transportation Safety Board (NTSB) (1989) *Aloha Airlines, Flight 243, Boeing 737-200, N73711, Near Maui, Hawaii, April 28, 1988* (Aircraft Accident Report NTSB/AAR–89/03), Washington D.C., NTSB.

National Transportation Safety Board (NTSB) (2003) *Natural Gas Pipeline Rupture and Fire Near Carlsbad, New Mexico, August 19, 2000* (Pipeline Accident Report NTSB/PAR–03/01), Washington D.C., NTSB.

ACKNOWLEDGEMENTS

Grateful acknowledgement is made to the following sources:

FIGURES

Figure 4.1(a): © Stock.Xchng/jordi boix.

Figure 4.1(b): Stock.Xchng/Alison Scott, www.kittywompus.com.

Figure 4.1(c): Stock.Xchng/Gian Cardit.

Figures 4.2, 4.45, 4.55–4.58, 4.60, 4.64–4.78 and 4.80–4.84: © Peter Lewis.

Figure 4.5: Courtesy of DNV.

Figure 4.6: Courtesy of Oceanic & Atmospheric Administration/US Department of Commerce.

Figure 4.7: *Pipeline Accident Report – Natural Gas Pipeline Rupture and Fire Near Carlsbad, New Mexico, August 19, 2000*, NTSB/PAR-03/01, US National Transportation Safety Board.

Figure 4.8: Stock.Xchng/bisgaard.

Figure 4.14: © Colin Gagg.

Figures 4.16 and 4.20ii: Courtesy of Jack Burdett Collection, Point Pleasant Presbyterian Church and River Museum.

Figures 4.17, 4.20i, 4.24, 4.26 and 4.30–4.34: *Highway Accident Report – Collapse of U.S. 35 Highway Bridge, Point Pleasant, West Virginia, December 15, 1967*, NTSB/HAR-71/01, US National Transportation Safety Board.

Figure 4.19: Courtesy of James Bashford/Gig Harbor Peninsula Historical Society & Museum.

Figure 4.21: Earl T. Kilmer Collection.

Figures 4.22 and 4.23: Courtesy of Gannett Fleming.

Figures 4.27 and 4.29: Reprinted with permission from the *Journal of Testing and Evaluation*, Vol. 1, No. 2, © ASTM International, 100 Barr Harbor Drive, West Conshohocken, PA 19428.

Figure 4.28: © John Bennett.

Figure 4.35: © Bettmann/Corbis.

Figures 4.36, 4.39 and 4.41–4.44: *Highway Accident Report – Collapse of a Suspended Span of Interstate Route 95 Over the Mianus River, Greenwich, Connecticut, June 28, 1983*, NTSB/HAR-84/03, US National Transportation Safety Board.

Figure 4.37: From www.wikimedia.org. Permission granted under the terms of the GNU Free Documentation Licence.

Figure 4.38:© Hank Morgan/Time Life Pictures/Getty Images.

Figures 4.46–4.48: From Bagnariol, D. (2003) *Sgt. Aubrey Cosens V.C. Memorial Bridge over the Montreal River at Latchford. Investigation of Failure: Final Report*, December 1 2003, Ontario Ministry of Transportation.

Figure 4.49: Black Star/Stockphoto.com.

Figures 4.50–4.53: *Aircraft Accident Report – Aloha Airlines, Flight 243, Boeing 737-200, N73711, Near Maui, Hawaii, April 28, 1988*, NTSB/AAR-89/03, US National Transportation Safety Board.

Figure 4.59: Taken from Lewis, P.R. and Hainsworth, S.V. (2006) 'Fuel line failure from stress corrosion cracking', *Engineering Failure Analysis*, vol. 13. Elsevier Science. Figure from ICI industrial fibres manual, Chemical properties of terylene and ICI nylon (1981).

Figures 4.61–4.63: © NASA.

COURSE TEAM ACKNOWLEDGEMENTS

This part was prepared for the course team by Peter Lewis.

T357 COURSE TEAM

Dr Michael Fitzpatrick (course team chair)

Andy Harding (course manager)

ACADEMIC STAFF

Dr Alun Armstrong

Professor Chris Earl

Dr Salih Gungor

Dr Peter Lewis

Dr Ed Murphy

Professor Adrian Demaid

Professor Lyndon Edwards

Michael Hush

Dr Jim Moffatt

Dr Martin Rist

EXTERNAL ASSESSOR

Professor Lindsay Greer, University of Cambridge

CONSULTANTS

David Sefton (critical reader)

SUPPORT STAFF

Debbie Derbyshire (course team secretary)

Stan Hiller

Pete Ledgard

Colin Gagg

Gordon Imlach

Rehana Malik

PRODUCTION TEAM

Kirsten Barnett

Philippa Broadbent

Teresa Cox

Daphne Cross

Vicky Eves

Carol Houghton

Margaret McManus

Lara Mynors

Lynn Short

Annette Booz

Lisa Carrick

Sarah Crompton

Anna Edgley-Smith

Chris French

Jonathan Martyn

Katie Meade

Deana Plummer

Susanne Umerski